Minibeast
Stages 1 &

A Unit for teachers

Published for the Schools Council by
Macdonald Educational, London and New York

© Schools Council Publications 1973

First impression 1973
Second impression (with amendments) 1974
Third impression (with amendments) 1975
Fourth impression (with amendments) 1976

ISBN 0 356 04106 9

Published by
Macdonald Educational
Holywell House
Worship Street
London EC2

850 Seventh Avenue
New York 10019

The chief author of this book is:

Sheila Parker

The other members of the Science 5/13 team are:

Len Ennever	Project Director
Albert James	Deputy Project Director
Wynne Harlen	Evaluator
Don Radford	
Roy Richards	
Mary Horn	

Made and printed by Waterlow (Dunstable) Limited

General preface

'Science 5/13' is a project sponsored jointly by the Schools Council, the Nuffield Foundation and the Scottish Education Department, and based at the University of Bristol School of Education. It aims at helping teachers to help children between the ages of five and thirteen years to learn science through first-hand experience using a variety of methods.

The Project produces books that comprise Units dealing with subject areas in which children are likely to conduct investigations. Some of these Units are supported by books of background information. The Units are linked by objectives that the Project team hopes children will attain through their work. The aims of the Project are explained in a general guide for teachers called *With objectives in mind,* which contains the Project's guide to Objectives for children learning science, reprinted at the back of each Unit.

Acknowledgements

The Project is deeply grateful to its many friends: to the local education authorities who have helped us work in their areas, to those of their staff who, acting as area representatives, have borne the heavy brunt of administering our trials, and to the teachers, heads and wardens who have been generous without stint in working with their children on our materials. The books we have written drew substance from the work they did for us, and it was through their critical appraisal that our materials reached their present form. For guidance, we had our sponsors, our Consultative Committee and, for support, in all our working, the University of Bristol. To all of them we acknowledge our many debts: their help has been invaluable.

Metrication

This has given us a great deal to think about. We have been given much good advice by well-informed friends, and we have consulted many reports by learned bodies. Following the advice and the reports whenever possible we have expressed quantities in metric units with Imperial units afterwards in square brackets if it seemed useful to state them so.

There are, however, some cases to which the recommendations are difficult to apply. For instance we have difficulty with units such as miles per hour (which has statutory force in this country) and with Imperial units that are still in current use for common commodities and, as far as we know, liable to remain so for some time. In these cases we have tried to use our common sense and, in order to make statements that are both accurate and helpful to teachers we have quoted Imperial measures followed by the appropriate metric equivalents in square brackets if it seemed sensible to give them.

Where we have quoted statements made by children, or given illustrations that are children's work, we have left unaltered the units in which the children worked—in any case some of these units were arbitrary.

Contents

1 Introduction

This book is about the 'creepy crawlies' of the animal world which fascinate children. Its content is restricted to what are technically termed invertebrate animals, but the restriction is an artificial one for young children. In their eyes a baby slow-worm is just as much a minibeast as is a fat wriggly earthworm, and a tadpole can justly share a minibeast label with a leech. We hope that classroom activity stemming from the Unit will reflect this viewpoint. We've selected invertebrate animals for treatment in the book not because we wish children to make an isolated study of them, but because their potential for first-hand observation and inquiry is generally less well known to teachers than is that of other animals.

The Unit is further concerned with attitudes to minibeasts since not all children will find them fascinating, nor indeed will all teachers. What delights one child may repel another, and within any one class there will be a mass of conflicting response. Some animals, particularly the colourful and active will appeal: others will not. And since children generally protect what they like and ignore or destroy what they don't like, the question of attitudes is important.

'I've found a ladybird—careful don't hurt it.'

'Ugh, here's a slug—shall I kill it?'

Every teacher will have particular attitudes to minibeasts that he wishes to encourage in children. They will guide his response in situations where children encounter the animals, and if formally expressed they represent certain objectives* he has for the children. He might, for

*For explanation and details see With objectives in mind.

example, want them to acquire *a sensitivity to the need to give living things proper care*' and will keep this objective in mind when the children are at work.

But children can achieve more from working with minibeasts than just developing desired attitudes and if they are to gain maximum benefit from their work the objectives the teacher holds for them are important.

Thinking about objectives

Let's consider what children might achieve through working with minibeasts. Besides certain *attitudes* what else might they acquire?

What *knowledge* can they gain?
What *skills* can they develop?
What *methods of working* can they experience?

By answering such questions every teacher can formulate particular objectives for his own class and with these in mind will be better able to take advantages of opportunities to achieve them, should opportunities arise.

Different teachers will produce different objectives and this is right because no one set of objectives could cater for all situations. Further, objectives are likely to change as work progresses. This is right too because objectives in no way represent a syllabus of work: they will change as classroom activities change. The approach is not 'these are my objectives, the children must achieve them come what may', but rather one allowing children's work to develop spontaneously with teachers aware of objectives relevant to new situations.

1

In the next chapter we will look at situations in which children start working with minibeasts and suggest relevant objectives. These and other objectives occur throughout the book. They function as they might in the classroom—important but unobtrusive guides to the why? underlying the what and how? of possibilities for children's work.

Getting help from the Unit

Help with activities

The Unit will be most helpful if you make frequent use of the subject index at the back of the book.

We have deliberately not collected in one place all ideas about work with particular animals. Such an arrangement would be very useful for the animal in question but it is not adequate for dealing with unknown animals. It also limits ideas for developing work which includes other animals.

Specific information about common animals is provided and indexed under the name of the animal but the Unit is organised around a more general appreciation of minibeasts. They are considered in terms of where they are found, what they do and how they might be kept in school. This arrangement is useful in two ways:

a. The indexing will help you put particular interests into a wider context.
Suppose, for example, some children are absorbed in watching caterpillars. Most likely they are intrigued by the way they move rather than the caterpillars as such. If you look up movement in the subject index you will locate ideas for developing their interest in terms of their particular caterpillar and also find suggestions which will lead to investigations of other animals.

b. The indexing will help you cope with unknown animals.
Even the most unpromising animal has some feature that can be investigated. Suppose, for example, a child brings in an inert animal and you have no idea what it is. Look up some general feature in the index, say colour or shape, and you will find suggestions that

may develop work outwards from a seeingly unprofitable starting point.

In this respect the arrangement of the Unit gives greater flexibility for use than would the mere cataloguing of information about individual animals. We hope this advantage outweighs any inconvenience caused by the need to consult the index frequently.

We suggest a preliminary reading of the book to give an overview of possible work; subsequently it is for 'dipping into'.

Help with objectives
In the Unit you will find frequent reference to objectives.* Let's put them in their intended perspective. A diagram may help:

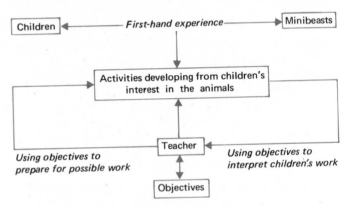

You will see from the diagram that objectives are not intended to dominate classroom work, but thinking about objectives can contribute to children's activities:
a. Helping teachers prepare for possible work.
b. Helping teachers interpret children's work in terms of what they achieve from their activities.

These ideas are developed in Chapter 2 and in Chapter 3, page 17, you will find a further example illustrating how thinking about a particular objective can stimulate ideas for work arising from children's interest.

---

*The objectives stated in the Unit are all taken from the Project's guide to 'Objectives for children learning science' which is reprinted at the back of the book.

2 Making a start

Considering starting points

Start with minibeasts brought in by children

Chance is on our side. There's a high probability that children will spontaneously bring small animals to school and here's an opportunity for the 'owner' to talk about his catch. Where did he catch it? How did he catch it? Were there others there? And why has he brought it in its particular container? Most children resort to pots with perforated lids—'so he can breathe'—with a supply of grass—'for him to eat'—and this vague appreciation of the animal's needs can promote fruitful discussion and investigation; as might the almost universal use of the descriptive 'he'.

Go on a minibeast hunt

If you work in a rural setting the possibilities are endless. If your school is in urban surroundings there's still plenty of scope. Chapter 3 gives practical suggestions about places to search.

Introduce some minibeasts into the classroom

If this is your starting point try to ensure that the minibeasts are exciting ones.

Here are some suggestions.

Bring in interest-capturing examples

Large woolly caterpillars, intriguing hawk-moth larvae and enormous hairy spiders are guaranteed to promote discussion and further activity. Local naturalists may help you obtain and make provision for them. Details of local societies are usually available in public libraries.

Provide animals that the children are unlikely to have seen before

Locusts are really exciting. Your local secondary school may have some you can borrow. The biologist will show you how to house and handle them. If you're bothered about handling them, don't worry because there will be at least one boy in the class who will take charge. If there are no local sources first check that you will be able to look after them (see Chapter 8) and then send away for half a dozen. Be sure to ask for male and female. Harris Biological Supplies Ltd, Winterstoke Road, Weston–super–Mare, will supply locusts practically by return of post.

Also consider *exotic butterflies*. You can order these from: Worldwide Butterflies Ltd, Overcompton, Sherborne, Dorset or The Butterfly Farm Ltd, Bilsington, Ashford, Kent. It's best to get these as pupae in early summer a short while before they emerge. Make sure you can keep them adequately (Chapter 8).

Arrange for local experts to visit the class with their minibeasts

A talk from an enthusiastic bee-keeper can stimulate much work. Make sure he brings some of his gear with him. Children love to try on his veiled hat, to look closely at honeycomb and above all see a demonstration of a bee 'smoker' in action. A visit to the hives will be full of interest. Flow chart 3, page 7, gives ideas for follow-up work.

Consider also the possibility of a visit from a Rentokil agent. If he comes armed with damaged wood, wood-worm beetles, plenty of 'fascinating facts' and pictures, it's a good start for upper juniors. It may lead to a general interest in beetles, a quest for other minibeasts which do damage, or to activities of the kind described in Chapter 4 of the Science 5/13 Unit, *Working with wood Stages 1 & 2.*

Finally, contacts with keen local naturalists are worth exploring; their enthusiasm will rub off on the children.

Getting work under way

Once children come in contact with minibeasts the essential requirements are time and talk. They need time to look and time to talk about their observations—talking to each other and in discussion with their teacher. What then develops depends to a large extent on how the teacher handles the situation; his response, and, in particular, his questions will greatly influence events.

Interested children will want to look closely at the animals, they may wish to keep them in school, and will most likely go hunting for more; but much of what happens will originate from their teacher, skilfully introduced to trigger off activity on the part of the children. Hence it is important for him to have a clear idea of his objectives for them, and 'pre-thinking' about possibilities will help him adjust to particular events as they occur.

Let's consider some likely classroom events in terms of the Stage 1 objectives we might keep in mind. (An explanation of stages is given in the guide to 'Objectives for children learning science' at the back of the book.)

Looking at minibeasts
Children observing a small animal respond fairly predictably. They make comment on structural features that interest them:

'It's like a car aerial'—snail's tentacle.

They notice things the animal does:
'Look it's rolled up'—woodlouse.

They are likely to poke and prod, exploring their effect on the animal and its effect on them, and probably they will want to know its name. Thus they are preoccupied with what it is, what it does, and how it affects them. In this situation our objectives might be:

Awareness of the structure and form of living things.

Familiarity with the names of living things.

Awareness of the characteristics of living things.

Sensitivity to the need for giving proper care to living things.

But the children's interests, like the animals they observe, will not be static. From a very general beginning other leads may develop. For example, 'what it is' may lead to comparison with other things or 'what it does' may lead them to investigate certain of its properties.

For these developments other objectives are relevant, for example:

Ability to group living and non-living things by observable attributes.

Awareness of the structure and form of living things

Ability to find answers to simple problems by investigation.

Appreciation of the need for measurement.

Whatever develops, the children will likely communicate their work to others in a variety of ways. Wanting to encourage a personal response to the animals, we will look for opportunity to develop in the children imaginative speech, creative writing, poetry and a wide range of visual expression. At the same time we can also encourage other methods of recording which will help them organise their observations, and which relate to objectives such as:

Ability to tabulate information and use tables.

Use of representational symbols for recording information on charts or block graphs.

Keeping minibeasts in the classroom

If children want to keep small animals in the classroom, teachers have two things to think about. One (discussed in Chapter 8) concerns practicalities—how shall we house them? what do they eat? what will happen at weekends? The other relates to making full use of the

Sensitivity to the need to give living things proper care

animals in classwork, and it is here that the idea of objectives may help. All the objectives listed earlier are relevant to the situation and, in addition, classroom animals over a period of time can help children achieve:

Awareness of seasonal changes in living things.

Ability to predict the effect of certain changes through observation of similar changes.

Further, setting up and maintaining the animals can help children develop *skill in manipulating tools and materials* and help in their *development of a concept of environment.*

Hunting for minibeasts

This can be a very profitable activity for teachers and children. It has its snags, particularly in relation to inappropriate collecting (discussed in the next chapter) but it is likely to yield a rich source of teaching material. All the previously mentioned objectives apply here and can help teachers at the planning stage, before they take their children hunting. Such a search, with its increased opportunity for studying a great number and a wide range of animals, will admit further objectives, for example:

Appreciation of the variety of living things and materials in the environment.

Formation of a broad idea of variation in living things.

Development of a concept of environment

Working with objectives in mind

Our suggested objectives are clearly not specific to small animals. Each one could be applied to any situation where children come in contact with living things and many would also do for children exploring non-living material. This is important, for *we are concerned not so much with what children can learn about small animals, but rather with what working with small animals can do for their understanding of science, and their personal development.* Hence our objectives are stated in general terms. And this is helpful. It means that teachers using objectives can work out a framework enabling day-to-day activities in science to slot into a wider pattern.

But thinking about objectives, with its emphasis on why we are doing these things, requires that classroom events must be interpreted in terms of what children might gain from their work.

Interpreting classroom work in terms of objectives

In the following examples some things that developed when children came into contact with minibeasts are recorded : teachers might like to consider the objectives involved.

Flow chart 1 shows what happened in a class of six-to-seven-year-olds.

Minibeasts kept this class busily occupied for about five weeks, though of course this was not the only work that went on in the classroom and all children were not equally involved all the time ; nor did interest die completely and suddenly at the end of this period.

The next example (Flow chart 2), shows what happened when a group of children within a class of eight-to-nine-year-olds became interested in small animals. In terms of objectives their work is very like that shown in Flow chart 1, though the situation and the animals were not identical.

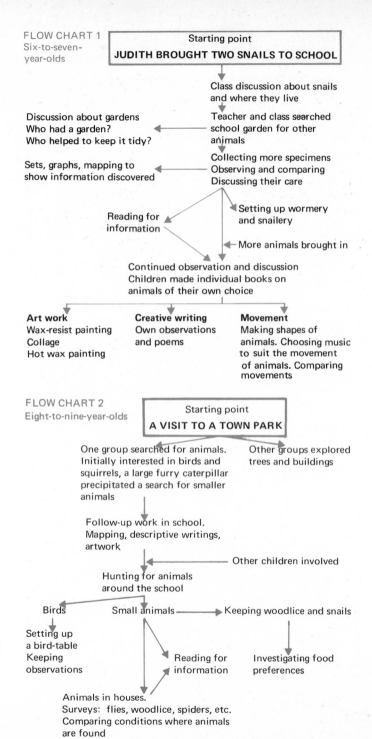

FLOW CHART 1
Six-to-seven-year-olds

Starting point
JUDITH BROUGHT TWO SNAILS TO SCHOOL

Class discussion about snails and where they live

Discussion about gardens
Who had a garden?
Who helped to keep it tidy?

Teacher and class searched school garden for other animals

Sets, graphs, mapping to show information discovered

Collecting more specimens
Observing and comparing
Discussing their care

Reading for information

Setting up wormery and snailery

More animals brought in

Continued observation and discussion
Children made individual books on animals of their own choice

Art work
Wax-resist painting
Collage
Hot wax painting

Creative writing
Own observations and poems

Movement
Making shapes of animals. Choosing music to suit the movement of animals. Comparing movements

FLOW CHART 2
Eight-to-nine-year-olds

Starting point
A VISIT TO A TOWN PARK

One group searched for animals. Initially interested in birds and squirrels, a large furry caterpillar precipitated a search for smaller animals

Other groups explored trees and buildings

Follow-up work in school. Mapping, descriptive writings, artwork

Other children involved

Hunting for animals around the school

Birds

Small animals

Keeping woodlice and snails

Setting up a bird-table
Keeping observations

Reading for information

Investigating food preferences

Animals in houses.
Surveys: flies, woodlice, spiders, etc.
Comparing conditions where animals are found

The basic similarity of the children's work in both examples is interesting for it illustrates a significant point. When children come in contact with new situations and materials they need opportunities for wide general exploration *whatever their age.* From such broad beginnings some will narrow their interests and may encompass work in which Stage 2 objectives apply. For example, the boys investigating the food preferences of snails (Flow chart 2) started with work because in the course of their general observations they noticed that their snails seemed to 'prefer' one kind of food more than others. Was this in fact so? How could they make a fair test for their ideas? In discussing and devising ways of attacking the problem these children gained experience that would help their *'appreciation of the need to control variables and use controls in investigations'.*

FLOW CHART 3   Ten-to-eleven-year-olds

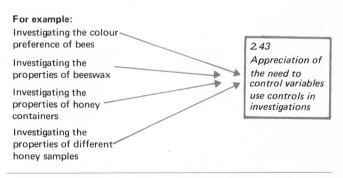

The development from Stage 1 to Stage 2 activities is not an overnight happening, and since it depends greatly on earlier experience, it cannot be tied to age. But a ten-year-old will have greater experience than a six-year-old, and so it is likely that more Stage 2 work will be in evidence in a classroom of older children. This is illustrated by the work of ten-to-eleven-year-olds who studied bees. Flow chart 3 contains several examples of development from Stage 1 activity and at the same time emphasises the eclectic approach so typical of this age.

What emerges from these case histories is the wide range of activities that engross children once their interest in small animals is captured. To make the most of their interest, to give guidance and help when it is needed, we must be aware of possible lines of development, bringing together the what, how and why of classroom events. These possibilities we will consider in subsequent chapters.

Thinking about the relationship between activities and objectives

Flow chart 3 summarises a range of activities centred on an interest in bees. At an immediate level it gives us information about what the children *did* but less obviously it also provides information about what the children *might have achieved* as a result of the activities. If we consider the case history in terms of objectives* some useful points arise.

1. Different activities can relate to the same objective

For example:

Investigating the colour preference of bees

Investigating the properties of beeswax

Investigating the properties of honey containers

Investigating the properties of different honey samples

> 2.43
> *Appreciation of the need to control variables use controls in investigations*

The objectives quoted and their notation are taken from the guide to 'Objectives for children learning science' reprinted at the back of the book.

2. Implicit in any one activity there are numerous objectives

Let's look at some of the Stage 2 objectives involved when the children made a model of a honeycomb.

2.02 Willingness to observe objectively.

2.05 Interest in choosing suitable means of expressing results and observations.

2.07 Willingness to examine critically the results of their own and other's work.

2.23 Recognition of similar and congruent shapes.

2.24 Awareness of symmetry in shapes and structures.

2.25 Awareness of internal structure in living and non-living things. .

ACTIVITY: MAKING A MODEL HONEYCOMB

Children were involved in:

measuring an actual comb; finding out about comb construction; choosing materials for their replica; manipulating materials; labelling finished model.

2.23 Appreciation of measurement as a division into regular parts and repeated comparisons with a unit.

2.33 Development of concepts of conservations of weight, area and volume.

2.51 Knowledge of conditions which promote change in living and non-living materials.

2.58 Skill in constructing and devising simple apparatus.

2.59 Ability to select relevant information from books and other reference material.

2.74 Ability to construct models as a means of recording observations.

2.86 Appreciation of the relationship of parts to wholes.

2.93 Awareness that many factors need to be considered when choosing a material for a particular use.

3. The relationship of objectives and activities is complex but its appreciation can add a new dimension to thinking about what goes on in the classroom

Here, for example, is an illustration of part of the activity-objective relationship operating when the children were working at their topic on bees.

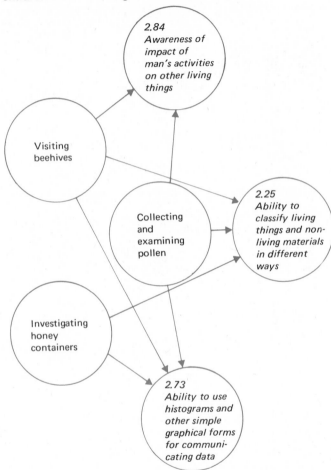

Thinking along these lines, like so many other things, does not come easily at first. But throughout the Unit objectives will occur again and again, either explicitly stated or implicitly there. In making use of the ideas relating to minibeasts and children's activities, the Project team hopes that teachers will gradually acquire the habit of working with objectives in mind.

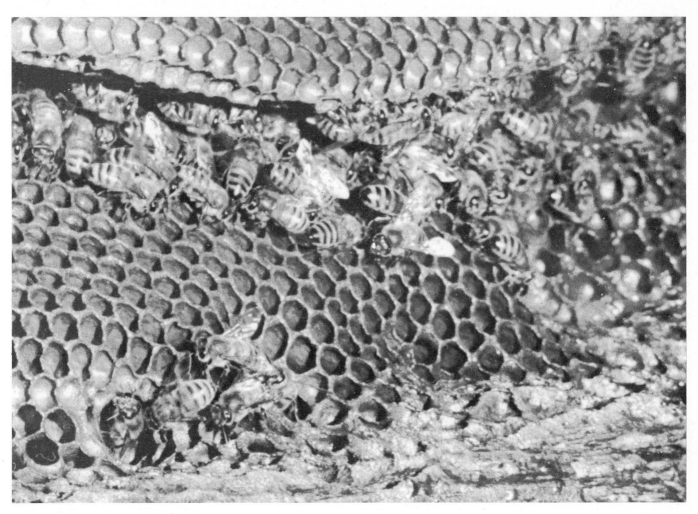

Bees in a natural hive in a tree

Along the sides of paths

Under stones

In the soil of flower beds

In flower heads and on the leaves of bushes

In guttering

In a lump of turf dug from the edge of the playing field

10

3 Where can we find them?

The short answer to this chapter heading is *everywhere*. And this is a daunting statement for many teachers. Some react—'Well, I haven't noticed'; others—'That's just what worries me, I can't cope.' But there are two points here:

1. Small animals are more or less everywhere, but we (and the children also) have to get our eye in and know where to look, before we appreciate the truth of the statement.

2. Even though these animals are abundant in numbers and kind, we can approach their study in ways bringing order to the apparent chaos of the unknown.

Knowing where to look

Search around the school
Have a discussion about responsible methods of searching (page 22) and encourage suggestions for places worth exploring.

Why not involve children in some of the illustrated activities?

Remember also that buildings can be productive places.

Get out and about
Country schools have no problems here. Hedgerows, ditches, ponds, orchards, woods and fields are teeming with minibeasts, though it sometimes needs a practised eye to detect them. Do encourage your children to become familiar with the common kinds in their surroundings and if they go on visits further afield— perhaps to a school camp in another area—provide opportunity for them to investigate the minibeasts

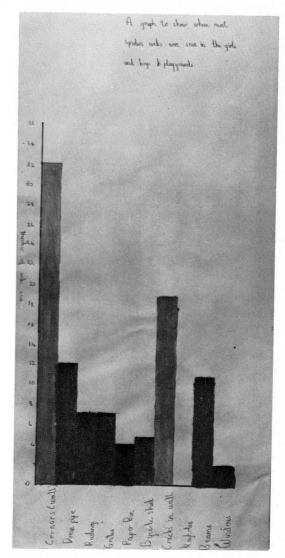

Where will we find spiders?

Old tree trunks are worth exploring

occuring there. Do they find the same kind? Can they find animals new to them?

Schools in urban areas will have less opportunity for minibeast hunting. But it's not impossible. Here's what happened in one city school:

EXPLORING WATER LIFE IN AN INDUSTRIAL CITY

Listing possible places using local knowledge of maps

Individual visits to convenient canals, park ponds, standing water on building sites, water troughs in gardens 'to see what's there'. (Many of these visits were made by an enthusiastic teacher collecting large buckets of water for later investigation in school)

Collecting and investigating polluted water

Has it any animal and plant life?
Which sample is dirtiest?
Can it be made clean?
How do detergents and other pollutants alter tap water?

Class visit to a canal containing minibeasts

(An interested parent accompanied the class to help in their supervision)
Collecting minibeasts for observation and investigation in the classroom

You will find other relevant suggestions in the diagram on page 21.

Note. In any activity of this kind there are two important safety considerations which children *must* appreciate:

1. The dangers of deep water. It's worthwhile paying particular attention to this in areas with unfenced water: instruction on water safety is very relevant.

2. The less obvious risks in handling polluted water. Children should wash their hands *thoroughly* after doing such work.

For all schools visits to *Nature Reserves* and *Nature Trails** are possible starting points. The children will not be able to collect animals but what they see on these visits often stimulates them to search nearer home.

It's surprising how many visits can lead into some aspect of studying minibeasts, even though they are organised for different purposes. Three examples will serve as illustrations:

One class visiting a *castle* discovered and developed interest in the many snails they found in cracks in a wall. Incidentally *old walls* wherever they occur are productive hunting grounds.

Another class on a *farm* visit were shown ticks and told about other minibeasts that affect domestic animals. This interest revealed itself later in follow-up work when a group prepared a talk on animals that live on other animals.

A visit to a *museum* to study rocks stimulated some children to search for minibeasts. They were fascinated by the colourful and grotesque tropical insects on display there and decided to explore insects in their own surroundings.

These examples are not quoted as a plea to introduce

Information about Nature Reserves and Nature Trails can be obtained from the Council for Nature and the Forestry Commission. It is also likely to be displayed in the public library.

minibeasts in all work: that would be too artificial and imposed. But wherever you go there will be minibeasts about and they may provide some children with points of developing interest.

Searching with a 'seeing eye'

Some situations are more productive of minibeasts than others, and teachers will find it useful to acquire a way of looking that will help them to appreciate good sources for their children's explorations.

Biologists give convenient classification tags to places where living things are found. They refer to them as habitats, and an appreciation of habitats can give us a profitable guide for finding useful places to explore.

There are two major habitats—terrestrial and aquatic— and minibeasts, of course, occur in both. Each major habitat can be subdivided almost infinitely and *as long as we remember that any such classification is merely a convenient way of organising a situation far from cut and dried,* this method of surveying habitats can be a useful start to knowing where to look.

We might consider some of the habitat possibilities as shown in the chart on the right.

The point of the lists is not that teachers should know about the animals in each particular habitat, but to illustrate a divisive principle that can be applied to any environment. It is a way of looking—of seeing, for example, a field of grass and, knowing that there will be animals there, of looking at the field in terms of its component parts. Each will likely yield something worth observing and, using this technique, things which escape a cursory search will emerge; a bracket fungus on a fence-post may reveal an interesting crop of beetles, or an uninspiring cowpat supply a fascinating range of animals for investigation.

Children, of course, will not normally use such systematic searching procedures; they tend to rush around flitting from place to place in search of the obvious. And their approach has much to commend it, for it allows work to develop from things of immediate interest. But somewhere along the way we might help them enlarge their sphere of operations, providing we ourselves are aware of all the possibilities of an area.

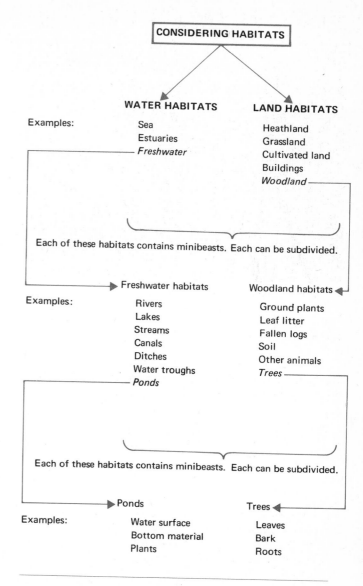

CONSIDERING HABITATS

WATER HABITATS   LAND HABITATS

Examples:

Sea	Heathland
Estuaries	Grassland
Freshwater	Cultivated land
	Buildings
	Woodland

Each of these habitats contains minibeasts. Each can be subdivided.

Freshwater habitats   Woodland habitats

Examples:

Rivers	Ground plants
Lakes	Leaf litter
Streams	Fallen logs
Canals	Soil
Ditches	Other animals
Water troughs	*Trees*
Ponds	

Each of these habitats contains minibeasts. Each can be subdivided.

Ponds   Trees

Examples:

Water surface	Leaves
Bottom material	Bark
Plants	Roots

Knowing when to look

Most places are worth visiting at any time of the year but much of our work will be seasonal. *Some* possibilities are outlined below for general guidance, but clearly conditions will vary enormously from place to place and year to year.

Autumn term

Hunt for minibeasts in fungi

Early

Search host plants for caterpillars. In particular look for hawkmoth larvae on apple, lime, poplar and privet. Hairy caterpillars, found on oak and birch for example, are also interesting 'finds'.
Note. Some hairy caterpillars cause a skin rash in sensitive individuals.

Examine fallen and over-ripe fruit.
Examine compost heaps, cowpats.
Examine fungi (particularly bracket fungi).
Note. Children should be able to recognise poisonous types and should treat *all* fungi with respect.
Make early morning visits to dew-laden webs.
Observe and investigate wasps.

Later

Hunt for galls which are conspicuous now leaves are shed. Oak trees are particularly productive.

Search cruciferous vegetables (cabbage, Brussels sprouts, kale) for minibeasts. Examine leaf litter. Look under stones.

Spring term

Look for pupae in the soil

Early

Dig for pupae under trees. Oak, ash, beech, elm are particularly good. Dig gently about 20–30 cm from the tree at a depth of about 10 cm and sieve the soil.

Hunt for cocoons (particularly in sheds, cellars, hollow trees, old buildings).
Make use of animals found in stored food (eg flour beetles).

Look for pupae under moss on trees and under flaking bark (particularly on the sheltered side of the trees).
Examine the bark on old dead branches and fallen logs for beetles, beetle larvae and the burrows of bark beetles.
Dig and sieve the soil of rough ground.

Later

Explore long grass on a warm day for insects, especially leaf hoppers.

Keep watch for butterflies.
Examine hedges (particularly hawthorn and bramble) for caterpillars. Look closely at the leaves and at ground level.

Look on the sheltered side of trees and fences for resting moths.
Visit a pond before the weed gets too thick for easy observations.

Summer term

Watch for dragonflies emerging

Early
Visit a pond in early morning for the chance of seeing dragonflies and damselflies emerge.
Investigate caddis larvae.

Look for caterpillars (especially on stinging nettles and cabbage).
Examine young leaves for leaf damage.
Investigate cuckoo spit.
Hunt for aphids.
Examine flowers, particularly umbelliferae (eg hogweed) and compositae (eg dandelion).

Later
Search for spiders' webs.

Observe flower visitors.
Hunt for caterpillars and ladybirds.
Visit a beehive.
Look under stones and logs.
Observe the flight of flying insects.
Investigate ants' nests.

Ideas for development

Taking children in search of small animals is a delightful occupation. Providing we make the right material provision everyone will find something of interest, and interests will not, of course, be confined to science. But of those that are, what will the children do after their initial interest? What preparation can teachers make to ensure productive work; particularly for those children who find it hard to get going?

The first requirement is that children should have opportunity and encouragement to observe their finds.

It's hard to overestimate the value of outdoor observations. Sometimes the observations will be complete in themselves—and let's not forget that children need time to 'stand and stare'—but often they suggest further activity. Yet children vary greatly in their powers of observation and in what they think about the things they notice. Some will observe, and be off on a self-chosen exploration: others will not. This second class of children needs particular guidance. They need help in observing, plenty of opportunity to discuss what they find and, frequently, stimulating questions to direct their interests before they can make a start on follow-up work.

Preparing for possibilities

Two things are helpful here:

1. Thinking about children's natural interests.

2. Thinking about objectives relevant to children searching for minibeasts.

Teachers will have no difficulty with the first, but some may find thoughts about the second less easy.

Let's develop the idea.

Consider for example some of the Stage 1 objectives mentioned in the previous chapter:

Awareness of the structure and form of living things.

Awareness of the variety of living things and materials in the environment.

Awareness of seasonal changes in living things.

Development of the concept of environment.

If we take children out and about observing a wide range of animals in differing places at different times we will provide experience likely to help children achieve these objectives.

But just precipitating children into the right situation will not necessarily ensure that they will achieve the objectives we have for them.

For objectives are not once and only things to be mastered at a single sitting. They can, and should, be approached in various ways and so we must think more about the nature of the children's experience.

If, for example, we wish to increase their *awareness of the structure and form of living things* we might consider the following questions:

What *interests* might focus their attention on structure and form?

What *activities* might then develop that would give them greater awareness of structure and form?

What *other activities* involving other materials relate to the same objective?

'Thinking through' objectives along these lines helps us to see potential lines of development which might be useful when the children are working.

Let's now select one objective very relevant for children hunting small animals, and consider it in practical terms.

Objective: Development of the concept of environment

1. What does the objective mean?
The concept of environment relates to interactions between living things and their environment, and environment is used as a collective term for the inter-related conditions in which an organism lives. It thus involves the *physical surroundings* of small animals

including less tangible things such as air, temperature, light and the other *living things* in the vicinity.

2. How might children achieve the objective?
A full understanding of the interaction between small animals and their environment is beyond the grasp of young children, but we can help them develop the concept if we give them plenty of opportunity to explore and talk about particular animals living in particular places.

3. What are the practical possibilities?
Some suggestions follow and numerical reference is made to other objectives using a notation which corresponds to the 'Statement of objectives' at the back of the book.

Exploring minibeasts in their environment
How many different *kinds* of animal can the children find?
Children will certainly not know the names of all the animals they encounter so it helps to emphasise what they can do, rather than what they may or may not know. 'Kinds of' is within the capacity of all children and can promote fruitful discussion of categories.

1.29
1.73
1.26

At an early stage the groupings will be very varied and, although not necessarily 'scientific' they will be right for the children. Later with a lot more experience 'kind of' can develop further (see Chapter 5).

2.25

Which animals are found in many places?
Which in few?
Links between animals and places might be made through discussion, through creative work or by organising the children's findings in various ways.

1.73
1.29

Listing things
Wide surveys For example:

Found under stones	Found on plants	Found on walls

1.75

Narrower surveys:
For example:

Found on cabbage plants	Found on stinging nettles	Found on leaves	Found on stems	Found on flowers

Mapping things
Using representational symbols such as sticky cut-outs and collage techniques.

1.74

Using non-representational symbols.

1.71

Making sets

1.29

Simple sets

Found in ponds

Found in streams

Overlapping

Pond

Stream

Complex overlaps

Found in air

Found on plants

Found on the ground

Making graphs

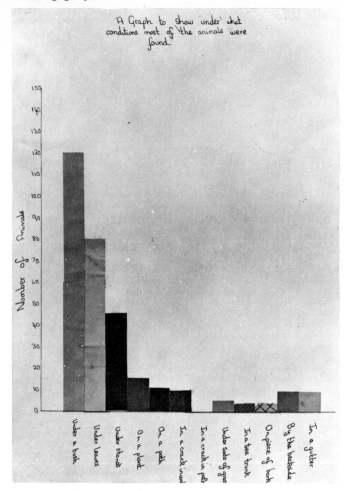

A Graph to show under what conditions most of the animals were found.

Number of Animals

(x-axis labels:) Under a bush · Under leaves · Under stones · On a plant · On a path · In a crack in wall · In a crack in path · Under soda of grass · In a tree trunk · On a piece of bark · By the bedside · In a gutter

How many animals can they find?

The number of animals occurring in different places may make interesting comparisons, but the findings should not be given too much significance. If seven spiders are found on one bush and five on another it's worth recording, but it doesn't necessarily mean that spiders 'prefer' to live on the most inhabited bush. Nor, of course, do ten worms in a bucket of soil represent one hundred worms in ten buckets' worth.

At an early stage estimations involving 'more than', 'less than', are best, though there is satisfaction in knowing exactly how many.

Later, children may enjoy tasks such as estimating the total number of animals in a particular place and the accompanying discussion of methods and their accuracy. They may need to devise tally systems for counting quick movers; perhaps they will have to invent ways of preventing animals being counted twice and, where numbers are too great, or the animals not so obvious, they may have to devise methods of sampling.

Will they notice the same things at different times?

Encourage discussion of the reliability of any records children make. Help them appreciate that their observations describe what they discover at any one time, but that at other times their findings might be quite different.

Will the kind and numbers of animals and the places where they are found be different:

At different times of the day?
Are any animals more commonly found in the morning than in the afternoon? What about at night?

At different times of the year?
If children go hunting during different seasons their experience, and any records they make, can be used for discussion and display of changes occurring during the year.

When the weather is different?
Seasonal changes, of course, apply here, but there will be opportunities to investigate shorter-term weather changes.

What is the commonest animal found on a sunny day? . . . on a rainy day?

Where is the commonest animal found on a sunny day? . . . on a rainy day?

In this work observations are good, but we must avoid facile explanations. Any differences discovered may relate largely to differences in the physical environment of the animals, but there may be other reasons.

At an early stage it is sufficient to note and talk about

In Dry Weather

	Spiders	Harvestmen	Woodlice	Beetles	Ants	Centipedes	Worms	Snails	Slugs	Earwigs
Leaf litter	3	5	6	2	none	5	2	2	1	none
Under stones	many	many	10	3	many	many	1	1	none	none
Rotten wood	6	4	many	none	few	7	none	none	none	none

In Damp Weather

	Spiders	Harvestmen	Woodlice	Beetles	Ants	Centipedes	Worms	Snails	Slugs	Earwigs
Leaf litter	3	none	many	none	none	3	1	17	4	none
Under stones	many	5	many	2	few	many	2	17	3	none
Rotten wood	3	none	many	none	none	2	none	4	2	many

things; later the children may perhaps attempt to correlate differences in animal distribution with differences in the physical state of the environment. (But the *reasons* why are sophisticated ones.) 2.41, 2.56

Will they find the same minibeasts living together in different places?
In this work we can develop the idea that particular habitats have characteristic animals associated with them. This is most apparent when very obviously contrasting places are explored.

Try comparing:

A flower-bed and waste ground.
A pond and a stream.
A lawn and long grass.
A ditch and a hedgerow. 2.91

Remember also that less obvious comparisons can yield much for experienced explorers.

Try:

A compost heap and garden soil.
A water-butt and an ornamental pond.

From a single comparative survey of what's there, work

might develop into an investigation of the physical conditions of the habitat, linking the findings with the occurrence of particular kinds of animals. 2.85

What's special about places where minibeasts are found?
Exploring their physical surroundings
Let the children consider some of the physical conditions in which the animals live. At an early stage this is best approached through discussion.

Is it: damp or dry?
light or dark?
warm or cold? 1.73

Exploring such things as long grass, leaf litter, rotting logs, young children can have lots of sensory 1.04 experience—looking, listening, touching, smelling. Comparisons are helpful.

Explore the feel of water at different depths.
Notice the differences between running and still water. Make observations at ground level on a lawn. Compare them with those made among long grass.

There will be much scope for creative work and any science is rightly wrapped up in a wider appreciation of the environment. From such beginnings more detailed investigations may emerge. For example:

How damp is damp? 2.41
How much damper is one place than another?
Is it always so?
What makes a place damp?
How much rain reaches it?
What happens then? etc, etc.

Gradually, children may gain greater awareness of the physical conditions in the environment of living things and more sophisticated work may emerge. For example:

Do different kinds of animals found in particular 2.91
physical conditions have any shared characteristics?
When the physical conditions change, do the animals change?
Do they do different things?
Do they alter in any way?

Looking at living things

Are there lots of living things, or few?
Are there animals that seem to live together?
Are there animals that seem to live alone?
Are there plants there? If so, do the minibeasts associate with them in any way—for protection? for food?
Are there signs of larger animals—tracks, fur, feathers, droppings, food remains?
Are there signs of man's activities?

The concept of environment is a complex one but through work of the kind outlined in this section we can help children to build up patterns in their observations that will benefit later understanding.

The 'thinking through' of the objective *development of the concept of environment* illustrates an important point. It is this:

By stating objectives for children, by considering what each means and by thinking of relevant practical experience children might have, we can prepare for profitable lines of inquiry, which could develop from their spontaneous interests.

Possible activities have been isolated in this chapter for greater clarity but it is important that such work is but part of a wider treatment emphasising the wholeness of the environment.

The following diagram shows how various lines of inquiry might interact when children explore a pond. It can be adapted for other habitats.

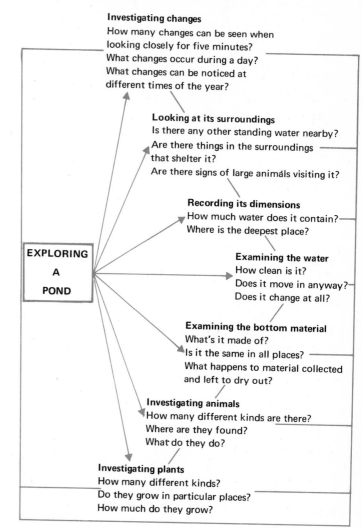

Investigating changes
How many changes can be seen when looking closely for five minutes?
What changes occur during a day?
What changes can be noticed at different times of the year?

Looking at its surroundings
Is there any other standing water nearby?
Are there things in the surroundings that shelter it?
Are there signs of large animals visiting it?

Recording its dimensions
How much water does it contain?
Where is the deepest place?

Examining the water
How clean is it?
Does it move in anyway?
Does it change at all?

Examining the bottom material
What's it made of?
Is it the same in all places?
What happens to material collected and left to dry out?

Investigating animals
How many different kinds are there?
Where are they found?
What do they do?

Investigating plants
How many different kinds?
Do they grow in particular places?
How much do they grow?

EXPLORING A POND

In the work that follows many of the objectives of the chapter will recur again, along with others. Teachers may find it helpful to 'think through' subsequent objectives in order to expand the practical suggestions of the Unit.

4 Shall we collect them?

A word of caution here. We need to curtail indiscriminate collecting without dampening interest, for children, however well-behaved, can wreak havoc among the small animal population of an area. Apart from any animals they remove, they can kill off hundreds by careless trampling and disruption of the animals' environment.

They need weaning from the idea that the best collection is the biggest one, and it is important to discuss with them responsible collecting methods.

Here are some guide lines:

a. What will a good collector do?

Help them appreciate that a good collector *searches carefully* and *disturbs the surroundings as little as possible.* Children often respond well to imaginative analogy here. 'If a visitor from outer space decided to collect people, how would they like it if . . .'

Emphasise also that a good collector *handles animals carefully* and *collects only a few;* though he may observe many.

b. When out of doors it's wise to show the children how to replace stones and logs they may turn over in their search and how to examine plants with care. It's also a good idea at the end of a hunt to organise a final look along the lines 'would anyone know we've been here?'

In any collecting activities we must keep in mind the objectives we have for the children, relating to attitudes. If, for example, we wish them to gain *'a sensitivity to the need to give living things proper care',* then we cannot allow them to collect animals just for collecting's sake. In this context it is helpful to develop the attitude that collections of *observations* can be just as valuable as actual specimens.

When animals are removed from their environment it should be because this is necessary in order to follow up a particular investigation arising from the children's exploration. Also children should be shown how best to handle their minibeasts. Small fingers might seem appropriate for small animals but they are not.

Collecting water animals

Looking for minibeasts on water plants

Do keep the following points in mind:

a. Protection of the children (see page 12). When exploring murky waters, the question of hygiene is

22

important. It's worthwhile taking polythene bottles of soapy water for hand rinsing. Certainly hand washing on return to school is recommended.

It's also advisable to take a towel—someone usually misjudges the height of his Wellington boots.

b. Concern for the minibeasts.

If the water is very fast moving, don't take animals back to keep in the classroom unless you can aerate them in some way. Running water has a higher oxygen content than still water, and many of its animals soon exhaust the oxygen in containers and so die.

All water animals need a supply of oxygen. They will not get it if collecting containers are full of water. One-third full of water is a good rule.

Finally, a mixed catch is best avoided, for a tube containing say, a dragonfly nymph and other animals may arrive at school with a well-fed dragonfly nymph as its sole occupant.

Collecting animals from still water
For shallow water, plastic gravy strainers make the best collecting equipment. They are not so unwieldy as traditional pond nets. But it's a good idea to take one long-handled net. It's useful for less accessible places— and for retrieving lost belts, etc.

Using a strainer:

i. Sweep it through the water.

ii. Tip it upside down over a shallow light-coloured container, eg pie dish, containing a little pond water.

iii. The contents of the sieve fall into the pie dish, any animals are clearly visible and can be removed. A plastic tea-strainer or spoon is good for this job and children soon become adept.

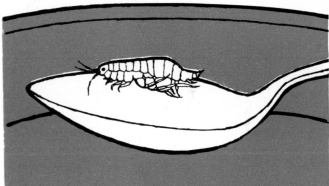

Wide-ended medicine droppers are best avoided unless youngsters can operate them proficiently. Too often when they are used the catch is drawn up into the bulb, which is squeezed with dire results for the animal.

iv. Collected animals can be transferred to suitable containers (chemists' tubes will do nicely) for transport back to school.

Animals attached to plants will not be caught with a strainer. Let children search for them by hand. They will need to look closely at such places as the undersides of leaves and the crevices where leaves and stems join.

They should not pull up plants indiscriminately, though they might remove a *few* common kinds without causing much harm. But plants take a long time to grow and if they are removed on a large scale the pond will be denuded of places for animals to shelter and, more seriously, of a valuable source of oxygen.

The bottom material of a pond is also worth exploring. Children might find ways of sifting mud to see what's there. Let them take some back to school and leave it standing in a jar containing pond water. They may see interesting things at a later date.

Collecting animals from running water

Here is a place where it is best to emphasise *observations.* In addition to the problem of keeping these animals alive in school, their indiscriminate collecting can dislodge many of them, sweeping them downstream to probable death.

Any collecting from running water should be done carefully. Many of the animals are adapted to withstand water currents and are commonly found under stones, attached to plants and in the bottom material.

Stone turning must be done gently. A net or square tin placed downstream will collect dislodged animals and the stone can be removed and examined for animal life.

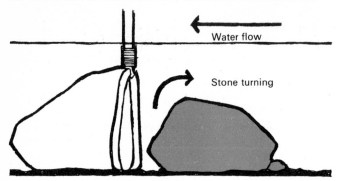

Net with wire frame bent to fit
the shape of the stream bottom

Stones must always be returned to their original position.

Hard-surfaced animals, such as snails and some caddis larvae, can be removed by hand. Others by gentle persuasion with a soft paint brush.

Collecting land animals

Searching by hand

In some cases, eg soil, leaf litter, small 'chunks' of the environment will be carried back in polythene bags for examination, but there will also be occasions for

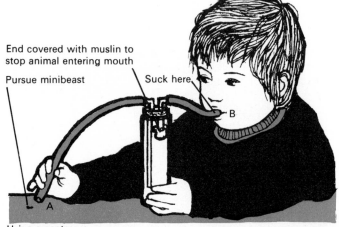

Using a pooter

collecting individual animals. Plastic spoons are useful here but for some small actively moving animals *pooters* are better.

Children pursue their quarry with end *A* and by sucking at *B* the catch is drawn into the collecting tube. If a number of identical tubes are available the tube can be corked for transport and the operative part of the pooter transferred to another tube for more collecting.

Using nets
Butterfly nets are popular with young children but in inexperienced hands can do a lot of damage to animals. For this reason it would be wise not to over-encourage their use. Yet they are often such ineffectual collecting instruments when used by children that it seems a pity to deny the pleasure of the chase, knowing that capture is not very likely. And let's remember that capturing *observations* of flying insects is a very worthwhile task.

Sweeping and beating
These collecting techniques should be used with discretion. When sweeping, a large net is moved quickly through plants (especially long grass) rather like sweeping with an old-fashioned besom. At certain times of the year the catch is prolific, and is almost certain to reveal animals not obvious when hand searching. The same is true of beating. Here a flat surface (tray, cloth) is put underneath plants (tree branch, hedges, shrubs) and the plants vigorously shaken or beaten so that the animals they contain fall and become visible.

Clearly in each case damage is done to the plants—and animals—and whilst the finds will certainly be of interest, the methods are not recommended for widespread use by children. The guide line here is . . . Can I justify it? Can I make good use of all I find?

Trapping

When children have carried out minibeast hunts, interesting discussions can develop about animals active at night. How could they investigate them?

Here are some suggestions made by children:

'You could use paper or something and see if there are marks on it in the morning.'

The idea led to a group making smoked paper* leaving it out at night and trying later to identify tracks.

'You could make holes and see if any animals fall in.'

Let the children try out this idea. They will encounter practical problems. How can they make sure the animals can't climb out? Is the shape of the container important? Is the material it is made from important? What's the best kind of material to use? How will they prevent rain or debris falling into their trap?

They may end up with something like the following pitfall trap:

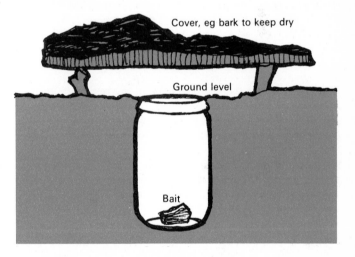

Cover, eg bark to keep dry

Ground level

Bait

'You could put out lots of food and they'd get full up and stay there all night.'

Let them explore this possibility. Try a range of bait: meat, fruit, juicy leaves and anything else they suggest. One class found that fruit pastilles collected a lot of ground beetles.

*Smoked paper is best prepared under supervision. A candle with a few drops of cycle oil dropped on the burning wick will produce black smoke which will darken paper.

They will have to find a way of anchoring their bait.

Anchorage (skewer, knitting needle, tent peg)

Bait

Will different kinds of bait attract different kinds of animals?

The value of this kind of work lies in discussion of the initial problem and the opportunity it offers for developing ideas and devising ways for investigating them. The suggestions outlined above *should not* be introduced as 'set pieces'. *Indiscriminate trapping just for trapping's sake should be avoided at all costs.* If promising ideas are suggested by the children, encourage their use on a limited scale but long-term trapping activities are best avoided.

Many other ingenious suggestions may come from children about collecting animals not readily accessible to them.

In one school a group made a kite with a long tail of sticky paper 'to catch minibeasts that fly high in the sky'. Its making engendered great enthusiasm and involved the problem of how to release the sticky tail at different heights. The fact that the first kite collected no animals was not a deterrent to their interest: they pursued a new-found interest in kites and flying things.

What ingenious ideas could develop from discussing the problem of trapping water animals that are active at night?

Making use of collections

When children bring back animals that interest them there are so many possibilities for follow-up work that it's useful to have in mind some over-all picture of productive lines of inquiry.

Here's one which indicates, in general terms, things children might do, and gives reference to detailed suggestions occurring elsewhere in the Unit.

Minibeasts brought back to the classroom

Lines of inquiry	General activities	Main source of detailed suggestions
Where were they found?	Making further exploration of habitats.	Chapter 3 pages 18-21
What do they look like?	Investigating colour, shape and special features. Making models.	Chapter 5 pages 31-35
What are they called?	Using reference books. Making and using keys.	Chapter 5 pages 40-41
What do they do?	Investigating movement, feeding and general behaviour.	Chapter 6 pages 42-48 pages 48-55 page 51
Can we breed some?	Finding out about life-cycles. Rearing minibeasts.	Chapter 7 Chapter 8
How shall we keep them?	Planning suitable housing. Constructing suitable 'cages'.	Chapter 8
Are they 'friends or foes'?	Finding out about beneficial minibeasts and pests. Collecting other examples.	Chapter 6 pages 54–55 Chapter 6 Chapter 4

It is not suggested that children should systematically work through all these lines of inquiry. They are merely guides for teachers to help them develop children's initial interest in a particular animal.

A model of a fly

5 What are they?

Children and teachers will find many animals they have never seen before, and the question 'what are they?' becomes significant. Children want to know names and teachers like to provide them. But it's no discouragement that we can't put a name to everything we find—people who can do this with certainty are rare individuals indeed. What matters is that we approach unknown animals with confidence. For the *ability to name living things* is but one of many objectives we have for children and so naming need not, and should not, receive undue prominence.

In practical terms this means adopting the approach: 'I'm not sure what it's called, but let's see what we can find out about it.' Encourage observations of the animal's special features since these will be useful for later identification and, most important, they offer opportunity for other immediate explorations. Of course, names are useful, especially when talking about a particular animal, but if the correct one is not known, why not let the children invent something suitable for easy reference:

'Our snail is a humbug snail because it has a dark brown and yellow shell in a lovely spiral.'

This is the key to profitable work. Concentrate on what can be observed and let a quest for names be an incidental activity.

Some objectives to keep in mind:

Stage 1
Awareness of the structure and form of living things.

Familiarity with names of living things and non-living materials.

Ability to group living and non-living things by observable attributes.

Ability to find answers to simple problems by investigation.

Forming a broad idea of variation in living things.

Stage 2
Awareness of structure–function relationship in parts of living things.

Appreciation of adaptation to environment.

Ability to frame questions likely to be answered through investigations.

Ability to construct and use keys for identification.

Observing minibeast features

Children will need lots of general observation to assimilate say the 'beetleness' of beetles, the 'snailiness' of snails. Encourage all kinds of model-making and visual interpretations that help them record their impressions. Some will be accurate representations, others imaginative.

In all such work we must be careful not to stultify interest by undue emphasis on technical terms or pedantic accuracy. A child who paints a caterpillar with two-dozen legs may not be scientifically accurate but he has certainly appreciated the 'legginess' of his caterpillar—a point which has greater biological

significance than the actual number of legs present. This is not to say that we should gloss over inaccurate observation, but that accuracy can arise from impressions and should not initially have too great a prominence. In the past, nature study has sometimes over-emphasised observation of structural detail based on a formal classification of animals. In terms of our objectives such observations have restricted value. Far better that any work involving 'What is it?' be conducted in a spirit of inquiry so that structural details emerge from wider issues and relevant interests.

Aids to looking*

Try to provide things that help children notice the features of their minibeasts. Have available:

Things that magnify
Lenses.
Magnifying glasses in all shapes and sizes.
Nature viewers.
A microscope providing three-dimensional viewing.
Microscopes with a range of magnification.

Details about recommended equipment will be found in Chapter 10.

The list may seem formidable, but many children have such things at home and may be willing to share them with others. Further, the items are lasting ones and make a sound investment for a school.

Here's a drawing produced as a result of close looking with a magnifying glass.

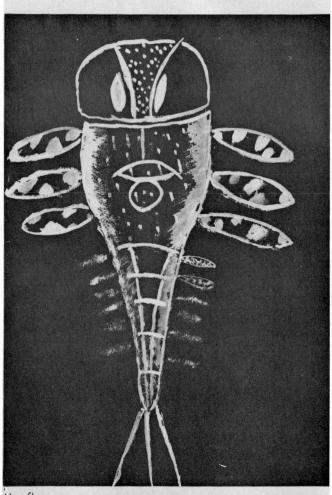

Mayfly

Things that make naked-eye observations easier
Stock up with white materials which give a good background against which to view most minibeasts, and remember that some animals are best seen against a

matt-black background.

An adjustable reading lamp may also prove useful.

Things that encourage observation from all angles

Have a supply of small transparent containers that can easily be held up to the light.

Acquire a few mirrors. Using these children may make interesting observations of minibeasts.

Things to notice

What shape is it?

What words best describe the shape?
Is it the same shape when seen from different angles?
Does its shape alter—when it moves?... during its lifetime?
Has it a symmetrical shape?
Can the children find other animals of similar shape?
How many different-shaped animals live in similar places?

These are general 'starters' that could apply to any minibeast, but sustained work is most likely when shape is a very obvious feature, as in the case of a snail's shell.

Let's take the example and pursue some lines of development:

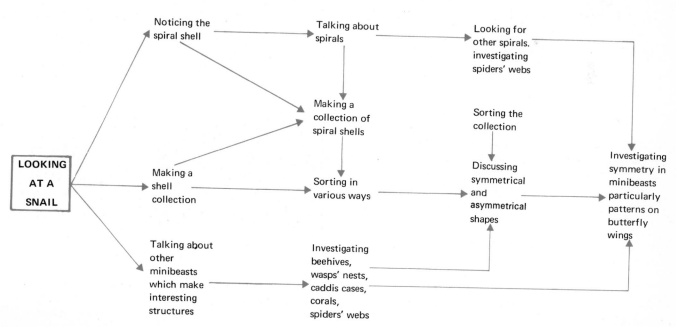

Symmetry in minibeast structures

There's enough work in the scheme on the previous page to keep children busy for weeks. Yet it is merely an outline of suggestions, any of which could lead to further lines of inquiry. Here are two:

Investigating honeycomb

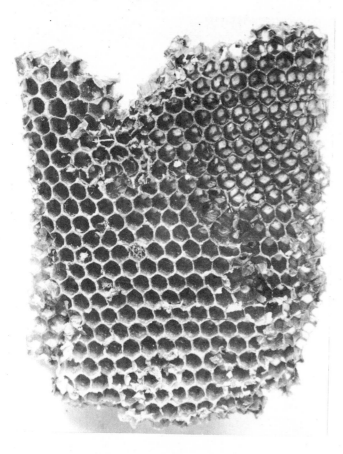

Try to get some material from a local beekeeper. It's most useful to have an empty frame (this is a man-made foundation of hexagonal shapes on which bees construct their cells) and a completed honeycomb.

Let the children examine the honeycomb carefully. How many cells are there? Encourage estimations, to be checked later by sampling or by actual counting. Have the bees made the same number of cells as on the original frame? Are all the cells the same size?

Could they make a model of a bee's cell? . . . of honeycomb? Let them explore possibilities. They may try paper, find it too 'floppy' and then use card.

Once they have a result that satisfies them other developments are possible.

Some might respond to the challenge of making a more permanent model. Be careful not to direct ideas too quickly for the value of the work lies in the devising of techniques. One group of ten-year-olds worried away at the problem for a long time and finally hit on the ingenious idea of casting plaster of Paris round wax hexagonal shapes and then melting the wax when the plaster was dry.

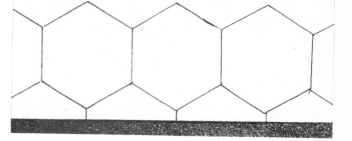

Today we finished our model honeycomb. We used wax candles and cut them into hexagons a half inch high. We used candles because they were quite easy to cut.

Once we had put the candles in some plaster of paris it set hard around them. Once the plaster was hard we heated the candle so that it would melt the candle — so we were left with the hexagon shapes.

We shall now be able to fill our cells with models of eggs, developing bees and different stores so that we can show children what a comb is like.

Children with a mathematical bent might explore further the shape of cells in the honeycomb.* Could they make an enlarged scale model of the cells?

Encourage them to investigate the way the open ends of the cells fit together. How would different shapes each with the same entrance perimeter fit together?

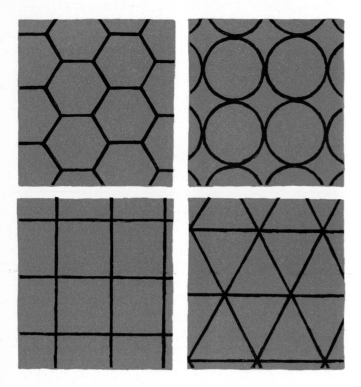

Which takes up most space?

If possible provide other examples of cell building in minibeasts:

Wasp's nests.
Hornet's nests.
The cells of solitary bees.

---

*Teachers with strong mathematical interests will find an interesting account in the section called the 'Bees Cell' given in D'Arcy Thompson on Growth and Form (abridged version), Cambridge University Press.

They make interesting comparisons.

Hive bees have vertical combs, with cells nearly horizontal.
Wasps build the 'other way up'. The combs are horizontal with upright cells pointing outwards from the nest.
Hornets build like wasps but the mouths of the cells point downwards into the nest.

Investigating caddis cases
Many caddis-fly larvae build cases with interesting shapes. They are water animals and if obtainable make fascinating studies.

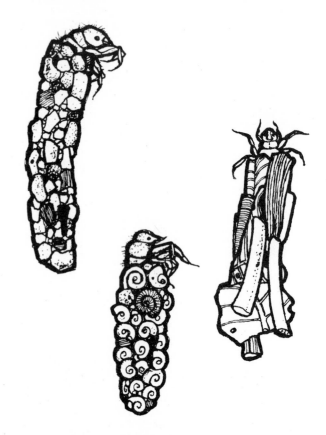

How many different kinds of case can the children discover?
Can they classify them according to the materials used to make a case?

Let them try separating an empty case into its separate parts. Could *they* build it up again?

If a larva is removed (gentle prodding at the rear of the case with a blunt instrument) will it return to its case?
If the case is broken up how long will the larva take to make a new one?
Will the second case have the same shape as the first?
If a larva without a case is given materials from the case of another kind will it use them?
If it's given an assortment of materials which will it 'choose' for a new case?
Could it make a case out of say, rice grains?

Work on caddis cases may develop into discussion of other minibeasts that are protected in some way:

What other protective structures can the children discover?
Which animals live in protected places?
Which are camouflaged?
Which behave in special ways when conditions are unfavourable?

What colour is it?

Is it the same colour all over?

Is it easy to see in the place where it is found?
Which colour background makes it most visible?
Which colour makes it least visible?*
Is it the same colour all the time?
Can they find other animals of similar colour?
Can they find animals that are a different colour at rest from when they are moving?
What is the commonest colour of the local animals?
What colour variation can they find in the same kind of animals? Banded snails and ladybirds make good subjects for investigation.
Is there any relationship between the colour of animals and the places where they live?

These are 'starters'. Why not try developing schemes for further possibilities of the kind outlined on page 31? Try 'thinking outwards' from a child's interest in a 'humbug' brown- and yellow-banded snail.

What are its measurements?

Can the children work out their minibeasts vital statistics? There's great scope here for discussing and devising techniques.

*You will find additional suggestions for work on camouflage in the Unit Coloured things Stages 1 & 2.

The peppered moths show interesting colour variation. The light coloured one was found in the country; the other has adapted to sooty industrial conditions

How heavy is it?

Is it as heavy as . . .? Is it heavier than . . .?
Encourage children to make their own weighing devices.

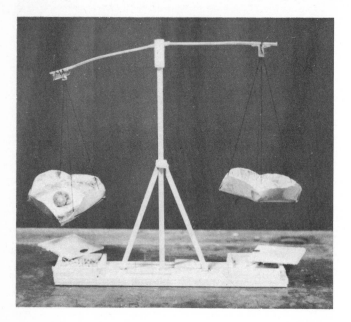

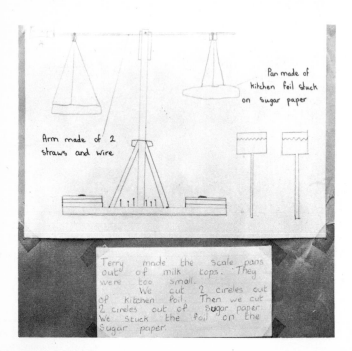

Pan made of
kitchen foil stuck
on sugar paper

Arm made of 2
straws and wire

Terry made the scale pans
out of milk tops. They
were too small.
We cut 2 cireles out
of kitchen foil. Then we cut
2 cireles out of sugar paper.
We stuck the foil on the
sugar paper.

How long is it?

This is an easy task for static minibeasts but what about minibeasts that change their shape or move quickly?

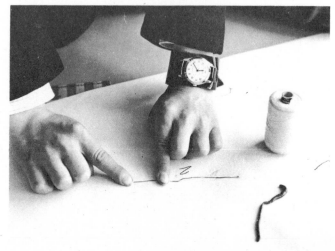

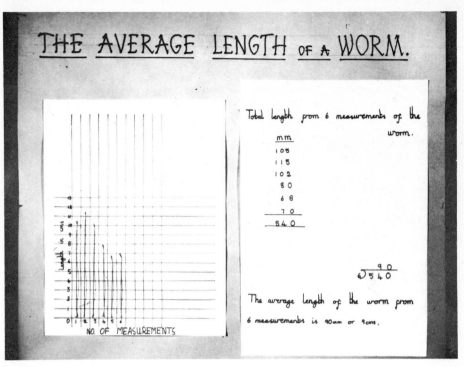

THE AVERAGE LENGTH OF A WORM.

Total length from 6 measurements of the worm.

mm
108
115
102
80
68
70
540

$$6\overline{)540}^{\,90}$$

The average length of the worm from 6 measurements is 90mm or 9cms.

How high off the ground is it?

Here's good opportunity for devising measuring techniques.

Can anyone find out from books, the name of the biggest minibeast alive today? Who can discover information about the biggest minibeasts that ever lived?*

Can they find other animals with exactly the same features?

Children can recognise differences in 'children', can they find differences in particular kinds of minibeasts? Could they pick out their minibeast in a crowd of similar animals?

A ladybird makes a good starting point. Children will readily comment on its colour and spots, and ladybirds are well-liked animals.

These were insects of the Carboniferous period. You will find details in children's encyclopedias with sections on prehistoric life.

How many spots has it got? Can they find others with more spots? . . . fewer spots? And exactly what colour is it? Are all ladybirds the same?

Over a period of time interested children can develop exciting work investigating the various spot number and colour combinations that occur in ladybirds.

Incidentally some children think that the number of spots indicates the animal's age. It's two years old. Next year it will have three spots.' Such a statement invites discussion. Is it true? Try breeding some to find out (see Chapter 7).

A search for differences within apparent sameness provides excellent opportunity for close observation and helps children appreciate that:

a. Animals they thought were the same are in fact different kinds of animals.

b. Animals of the same kind vary in appearance.

Biologically this is important experience of specific and individual variation in animals. But for children it's

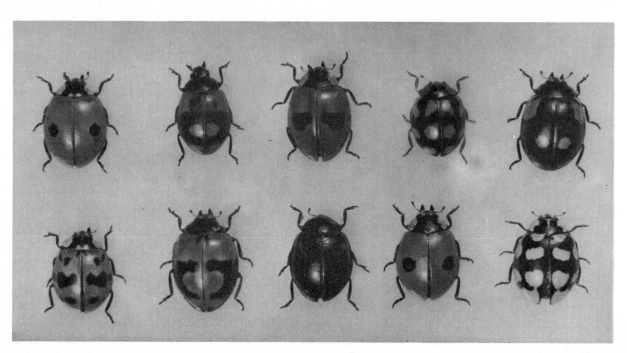

best to avoid such terms and regard the work as valuable for increasing their general *appreciation of the variety of living things.*

Worms and woodlice can also lead to sustained studies, though differences are harder to spot.

For a child a worm is just a worm, yet there are over thirty different kinds of worm found in Britain. Are there different kinds in the school surroundings? Encourage the children to look closely. They may notice general colour differences, differences in the shape of the tail end and differences in the position and colour of the saddle.

Work of this nature is not just an exercise in observation: it often triggers off spontaneous comments worth exploring further.

'We think worms with different colours live in different coloured soil.'

'We think worms with flat ends live furthest down in the ground.'

'They (woodlice) are different at the end. I think this one is commonest.'

A quest for 'difference in sameness' might involve explorations of differences in similar parts of various minibeasts. Insect legs, insect 'feelers' (antennae), insect wings all make profitable studies. And 'sameness within difference' is also worth pursuing. Try comparing various minibeasts with much larger animals, including the children themselves.

To conclude this section on minibeast features, do remember that close observations can stimulate creative work.

Our concern has been with children looking at minibeasts: interesting imaginative writing can develop from considering how minibeasts see children.

Naming minibeasts

One of our objectives for the children is the 'ability to name living things', and wherever possible we should help them enlarge their knowledge in this respect. But naming is not something to be formally taught; it should arise incidentally as part and parcel of other work. The snag is that some of the animals are extraordinarily difficult for children to identify and the role of the teacher is important here.

For very young children it's sufficient to place unknown animals into broad categories, for example, snails, worms, insects, spiders, but as they gain more experience we can help them enlarge and organise these initial categories. This means that teachers should try to gain a working knowledge of the animals their children are likely to encounter: not to be able to name everything, but to have a clear idea of how an unknown animal fits into a general pattern of identification. (The guide lines of Chapter 9 will help here and additional assistance can be obtained from local experts.)

With such knowledge teachers can produce material tailored to local needs.

Charts and cards

Found on the WATER SURFACE.

It may be:
A water measurer
A water cricket
A pond skater.

⑦
Check its name.

Look at page 69 of the Observer book of pond life.
Is it one of these?
If you think so, use its name and find it in the index of our other books. Check again using these books.
If it's not one of these use CARD

Charts or cards prepared by teachers and linked to available reference books, have great value in the classroom.

The photograph shows a chart prepared for nine-to-ten-year-olds. It is one of several grouped according to where the children found their minibeasts.

Keys
Some teachers have found it useful to construct simple keys for older children to use.

Here is the start of a comprehensive key made for top juniors who had access to a small pond. The complete key will be found in Chapter 9, page 85.

WHAT HAVE YOU FOUND?		
1.	Has it a shell?	
	Yes	2
	No	3
2.	What is the shape of the shell?	
	Raised coil = POND SNAIL	
	Flat coil = RAMSHORN SNAIL	
3.	Is the body made up of different sections?	
	Yes	4
	No = FLATWORM	
4.	Has it legs?	
	Yes	5
	No	20

Many children like the 'detective' approach to keys and delight in their use. The examples given could be used as a pattern for other keys. For example:

Common animals found in a local hedgerow.
Animals in a school garden.

Of course they need not be so comprehensive; a set of smaller keys can be very effective. For example:

Slugs and snails.
Caterpillars.
Animals found on the surface of water.

Children will need initial help in using such keys. They need to appreciate the linking function of the numbers, but once this is mastered they have acquired a powerful tool for identification.

For small keys the information could be linked by visual symbols, or colour-coded for easier use. Such a key made for ten-year-olds is shown below.

Some children might like to construct their own keys for others to use, although this is a difficult task for minibeasts since their features are so small. It is much easier with larger static material, and suggestions about the way children might set about key-making (which could be applied to small animals) will be found in the Project's Unit on *Trees Stages 1 & 2*

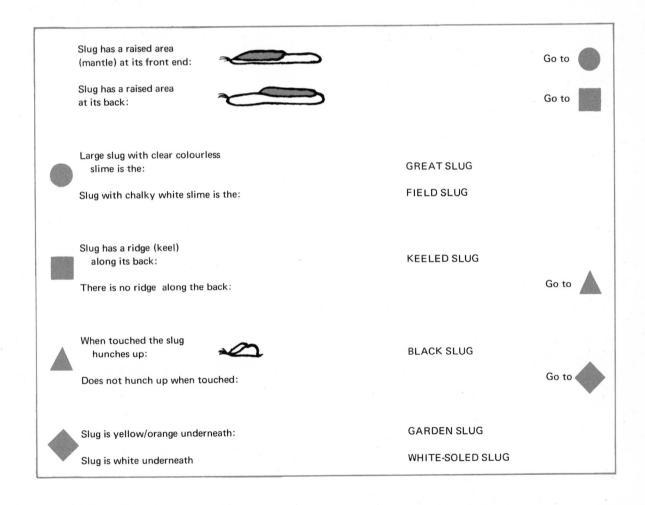

Symbol-coded key for identifying common slugs

6 What do they do?

Minibeasts are most exciting to children when they *do* something. Fortunately they do many things which offer opportunities for investigation. But remembering our earlier objective *'sensitivity to the need to give living things proper care'* it is important that the animals are treated with respect. *Minibeasts are not expendable.* Provided teachers and children keep this statement in mind all practical activities in the section can be carried out with no ill effects to the animals. But since many of the suggestions are stated as questions only, if children elect to find ways of answering these questions, then they and their teacher must discuss how they shall go about their task. They will need to pay particular attention to such things as:

Careful handling of all animals.
Making sure the animals do not encounter abnormal conditions for any length of time.
Making sure that after every investigation the animals are returned to a suitable place—either to their natural outdoor surroundings or to suitable classroom housing (see Chapter 8).

Any work on what minibeasts do relates, of course, to other studies. In this chapter we will consider their more obvious functions; their movement and their feeding.

Some objectives to keep in mind.

Stage 1
Awareness of the characteristics of living things.

Appreciation of the variety of living things and materials in the environment.

Ability to group living and non-living things by observable attributes.

Ability to find answers to simple problems by investigation.

Ability to tabulate information and use tables.

Stage 2
Awareness of structure–function relationships in parts of living things.

Appreciation of adaptation to environment.

Recognition of the role of chance in making measurements and experiments.

Appreciation of the need to control variables and use controls in investigations.

Ability to use histograms and other simple graphical forms for communicating data.

Appreciation of interdependence among living things.

Investigating movement

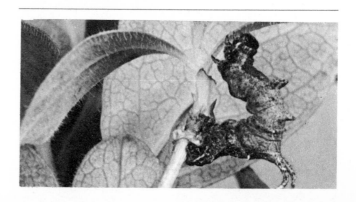

Looking at moving minibeasts

'It moves its body from side to side as if it itches'.
Christine watching a millipede.

'It moves like a tired old man but if you look underneath you will get a surprise. It's busy all the time.' Barry observing a snail.

How do they move?

What words best describe a minibeast's movement? Children can walk, run, hop, swim . . . can they find a minibeast with more than one kind of movement? How many different kinds of movement can they find by looking at various minibeasts?

Try to provide a range of different types:

Looping leeches and caterpillars.

Millipedes 'playing scales'.

Sliding snails and slugs. This is best seen by allowing them to walk over a sheet of glass and looking at their movement through the glass.

The peculiar movement of earthworms—are they really 'wriggly'?

'Busy' beetles, particularly aquatic whirligigs.

Various flying animals—do they all fly with the same movement?

The movements of animals that live on the surface of water.

If a projector with a Perspex cell attachment for holding water is available it is well worth showing children the movement of some of the smaller pond animals. The projector should not be left running for too long a period of time for the observation cell may heat up and damage the animals it contains. Watching the shadow shapes of say daphnia, hydra, leeches, freshwater worms, is an unforgettable experience and one likely to trigger off exciting creative work.

What words best describe various movements? Can they *hear* the animals moving? Try providing different surfaces for the animals to move over.

Can they select music appropriate to different movements? Can they imitate these movements?

Here is one teacher's account of dance/drama/music activities that developed as a result of looking at minibeasts.

'The song* was sung using children playing melodicas, recorders, and percussion as introduction, accompaniment and finale. After a discussion about the Insect World a class drama lesson followed in the hall. I spoke the images—such as:

"Insect world awake; hum their tiny song; climb the totter grass huge as mighty oaks to them,"

whilst the children acted out their individual ideas. The idea was repeated. This experience resulted in a group asking to make up their own music and in quite a number of children asking to make up a dance. Two groups were formed to create "The dance of the insects". The resultant music and dance was developed by the children themselves, with only a little help, and performed to the rest of the class.'

Encourage comparison of the movement of minibeasts with other movements. Have a look at domestic and other 'maxibeasts'—particularly zoo animals if this is possible. Note especially the ways in which the body is held off the ground, the construction of limbs and the range and speed of movements.

Wide observational experience of this nature can promote fruitful discussions from which general ideas about animal movement may develop. For example:

That there is a push against something to get movement in the opposite direction.

That, in general, flesh-eaters move faster than plant-eaters.

---

*The Insect World *by Richard Rodney Bennett.
Universal Edition IE 14167 Song no. 1.*

Comparisons with a wide range of non-living movement can also lead to useful discussion and investigation, and children might come to appreciate the need for energy in order that movement can take place.

Try comparing:

A beetle and a clockwork mouse.
A slug and a friction car.
A woodlouse and a robot.

How fast do they move?

An interesting problem for children. Familiar with the timing of racing events some may suggest finding out how long an animal takes to cover a given distance. This may be possible with certain animals such as caterpillars moving along a path, but in general minibeasts will not be so obliging. The children will have to devise ways of measuring the total distance covered by animals which constantly change direction (one nine-year-old pursued a centipede with a pencil; another got his snail to leave a trail on black paper) and find a method of measuring the total time of likely stop-start movement. There's scope for much ingenuity here and opportunity for discussing how accurate the results are.

Whose ant moves fastest?

Some children enjoy expressing their findings in miles per hour (perhaps kilometres per hour now). Many will enjoy holding snail, slug or caterpillar races.

Let's have a slug race

How far do they move?

Children could mark animals to tackle this problem. Snails are probably most suitable as a blob of distinguishing non-toxic paint can be put on their shells.

Perhaps someone knows of a place where lots of snails occur—old walls are likely spots. The inhabitants could be marked and investigations made.

If a snail is taken to a place, say 10 m from the wall will it find its way back?

If so, will it do this from 20 m, 30 m . . . ?

Do the snails move out on their own during the day?

Perhaps they move at night. Children might profitably discuss ways of investigating this.

Keen investigators will discover the 'homing' activity of snails which return after feeding to a particular place.

How do the snails 'know' how to get 'home'?

Can they see it? Can they smell it?

Do they follow their own trails?

Perhaps the particular ground they move over gives them the necessary information?

There's scope here for further investigation.

What happens if the children disguise the 'home'? Could they change its smell, remove any trails, alter the ground?

Does their movement alter?

Children who have closely observed small animals will come to recognise their characteristic movements. Discussing things which affect their own movements, for example different surfaces, hills, obstructions, they might devise situations likely to affect the movement of minibeasts.

Investigating land animals

Does an animal's movement alter on different surfaces?*

Can they observe animals whose movements alter when they carry things? Ants are good examples.

What is the steepest slope an animal can move up or move down?

What happens when a snail meets water?

See Chapter 10 for suggestions.

What is the widest gap it can cross?

What happens if it meets a stream or pool of water?

What happens if it meets other animals—of the same kind? of a different kind?

What happens if it meets various objects in its path?

Do animals 'know' what is in front of them? Can they see? Can they hear? . . . (see page 52).

Do different weather conditions alter the movement of minibeasts?

Do they move more in dry or damp conditions?

Do they move more in warm or cold surroundings?

Do they move more in light or dark surroundings?

Many children will be familiar with the movement of insects, particularly moths, around street lights and here's opportunity for further investigation. Are all minibeasts attracted to light?

The children will need to devise a 'light box'—perhaps a shoebox painted inside with matt paint—having a single source of light. They must discuss ways of finding out how the animal inside moves. Perhaps they can lift the lid and peep—perhaps they can find a way of recording the animal's tracks. Sooty paper (see page 25) or sand are two possibilities.

Careful selection of material will produce interesting results. Try using maggots, worms, slugs, beetles, ants.

Investigating water animals

Look at animals on the surface of water.

Investigate the 'skin' of water.

What things can they discover that float *on* the surface?

What happens to the objects if the surface is disturbed?

What happens if the water is polluted? If, for example, detergent is added to the surface?

How might their discoveries relate to animals that move on the water surface?

Look at animals in moving water.

Is there any connection between the direction of the current and the direction of the animal's movement?

Could the children simulate a stream by running water down an inclined surface?

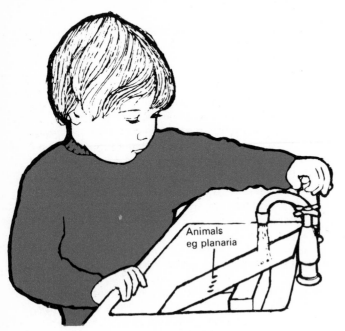

Animals
eg planaria

Lots of discussion will be needed here.

The children might investigate a number of different animals that they find in contact with stones on the stream bed. Planaria (small black or greyish 'blobs' up to about 1 cm long) make good subjects.

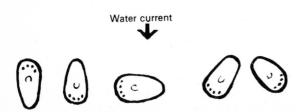

Water current

What happens if the animals are orientated in various directions to the water current?

Does the speed of the water affect animal's movements? This can be investigated in the classroom using a simulated stream. There might also be a small stream handy for field observations.

Are there places where water moves slowly/moves quickly? How slowly? How quickly?

Can they invent ways of measuring the speed of the water?

Can they find animals that occur in both slow- and fast-moving water? If so, can they notice any similarities and differences in the animal's movement in the contrasting places?

Can they find animals that only occur in fast-moving water?

A general comparison of the inhabitants of moving and static water is very profitable.

Observing moving parts
Do any parts move when the animal is not moving from place to place?

Which parts move when the animal moves?

Such questions lead to close observation and interesting discoveries. They can also promote comparative studies.

Looking at heads
Encourage observations of the exploratory movements of 'feelers' (antennae). The observations may suggest further investigation.

Can anyone find a minibeast with moving eyes?

Encourage observations of feeding movements. The children will need to look for 'something going on' at the head end and will be helped by using magnifying glasses. They can look for 'munching' movements and tubes leading from the animal to a food plant.

Some suggestions

Caterpillars snipping cabbage leaves.

Snails rasping away at plants. Water snails scraping algae from the sides of an aquarium are easy to observe.

Aphids sucking up plant sap through a piercing tube.

Flies and butterflies extending their probosces to suck up food.

Looking at legs

Is there any pattern to the way different minibeasts use their legs?

Children might use models here to investigate insect movement. Can they make a polystyrene 'insect' with six legs of pipe-cleaners or straws and find ways of using the legs so that it moves forward without falling over?

Can they discover differences in the legs of 'crawlers' and 'jumpers'?

Caterpillars also make good subjects for investigation. Is there any pattern to their movement? Are all the 'legs' used for moving?

How do legless animals move from place to place?

Investigate animals that move with the whole length of their body in contact with the ground, and animals that hold the body off the ground in some way.

Looking at wings

Here's what the famous English biologist Robert Hooke wrote in 1665 in his observation of the structure and motion of the wings of flies.* It may give teachers some ideas to follow.

'What the vibrative motion of the wings is, and after what manner they are moved I have endeavoured by many trials to find out . . . I endeavoured to observe several of those kind of small spinning flies which will naturally suspend themselves as it were, pois'd and steady in one place of the air without rising or falling, or moving forwards or backwards; for by looking down on those, I could by a kind of faint shadow perceive the utmost extremes of the vibrative motion of their wings, which shadow whilst they endeavoured to suspend themselves was not very long, but when they endeavoured to flie forward, it was somewhat longer.'

Hooke describes further investigations of the movement of flies' wings and then writes:

'And these vibrations . . . seem so swift that tis very probable (from the sound it affords, if it be compar'd with the vibration of a musical string, tuned unison to it) it makes many hundreds, if not some thousands of vibrations in a second minute of time. And if we be allowed to guess from the sound, the wing of a Bee is yet more swift for the tone is much more acute.'

The observation concludes:

'This subject had I time, would afford excellent matter for the contemplation of the nature of wings and flying.

Perhaps children could contemplate? They might also find out more about Hooke.

---

*R. Hooke, Micrographica, Dover Publications. A difficult book to read but if dipped into it may well suggest other inquiries.

Looking at respiratory movements

Encourage observations of the breathing hole of slugs and snails. How often does it open? Is its rate of opening and closing the same in different animals? Is it the same for a particular animal at all times? Try making records using a snail that has been stationary for some time and then again after it has been moving.

Some children get very interested in how minibeasts 'breathe'. This makes a profitable study. Observe the gills of water shrimps; find out about water spiders and diving beetles. But remember minibeast 'breathing' involves a difficult concept for young children. They identify it with their own lungs and breathing movements. Technically breathing is but part of the process of *respiration* by which oxygen is carried to all parts of the body, and although all animals respire, not all animals breathe. It might seem too purist to make this point for work with young children, but since most are familiar with artificial respiration it might be possible for teachers to unobtrusively substitute respire for breathe, and so help their later understanding of this important biological process.

This significance of taking in and using oxygen is beyond the grasp of young children but we might help those interested in this aspect of minibeast activity build up the following general picture:

The animals they encounter need air (oxygen).

Some have special places where the air (oxygen) enters the body. Slugs and snails, insects, spiders and woodlice are examples.

Some have special movements that help the air (oxygen) to enter.

Those animals with no special respiratory structures probably (in the children's terms) take in air (oxygen) all over their body.

Investigating feeding

Making observations
Watch minibeasts feeding

Encourage first-hand experience. You will find some suggestions for observing plant-eaters on page 46.

48

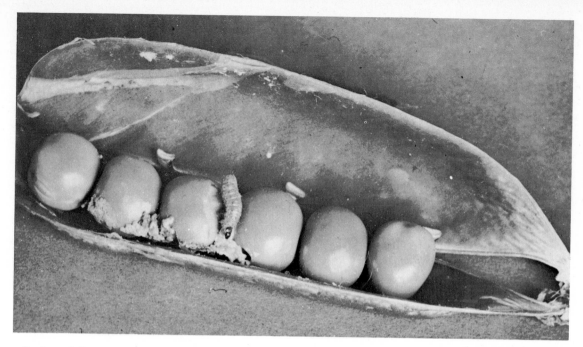

Can anyone find a minibeast feeding on animal food?

Spiders are worth watching. Go on a web hunt. How many different kinds can the children find? Is the web inhabited?

Just because the web is empty it does not necessarily mean that the spider is absent. It is probably lurking hidden at the end of a 'telegraph wire' which careful observers may notice leading from the web. A *gentle* touch of this wire, or part of the main web, may bring the spider into view.

Are there signs of previous meals?

What happens when a flying insect touches the web?

What happens if the web is slightly damaged?

Encourage children to collect *observations* of spiders in their webs. Can anyone describe how a spider feeds on a fly? Has anyone seen how a spider deals with a wasp that gets caught in its web?

Try collecting an orb web on a wire loop and support it indoors for further observations. Provide some shelter for the spider.

Is the spider most often seen in any particular place?

What happens if the web's position is changed? If it is turned upside down? If it is inclined at an angle?

Is the web material the same all over?

How strong is it?

Can the children make a web?

If two different spiders have their webs exchanged what will they do?

A young garden spider, given space and anchorage, will make a web in captivity (see Chapter 8).

If the spider makes a second web, will it make it identical to the first?

Will the web structure alter if the spider has more space? If more supports are available?

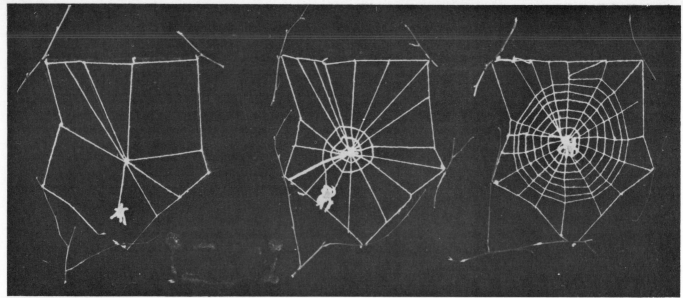
String models of web making

Can anyone catch flies to keep the spider well fed?
Some children become very adept at this: all attempts
offer opportunity for further work. How can they
approach a fly so that it doesn't 'know' they are
coming? Can it hear?...see?...feel?...smell?
its attacker?

Look for signs of feeding
A detective hunt is a good idea.

Collect damaged leaves. Look for leaves with holes in
them, and leaves with ragged edges. Can anyone
discover which animal has caused the damage?
Search for blotchy leaves. These may indicate the
feeding of leaf miners (holly and rose plants are a good

source). If the leaves are held up to the light the tiny
larva can be seen eating its way out of the leaf—unless
it has already reached the outside and departed!

50

Look for tunnelled bark on old logs. The inside of the bark may show signs of bark-tunnelling beetles. The central tunnel is made by the female in which she lays eggs, and side tunnels by the young larvae.

Be on the look-out for signs of worms feeding. Particularly in short grass children might discover leaves being pulled down into the burrows and will notice the worm casts which have passed through the worms.

Make a note of 'skeletons' in old webs.

How much do they eat?

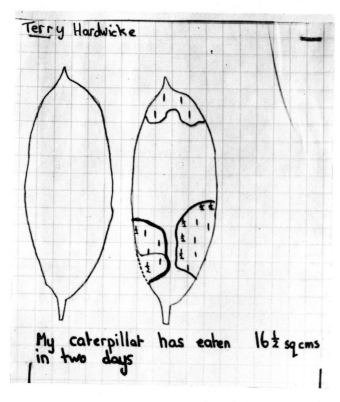

Caterpillars and slugs or snails make good subjects for investigation. If they are starved for a couple of days they will attack fresh food with gusto and the children can use squared paper to work out the area of leaf eaten in a certain period of time.

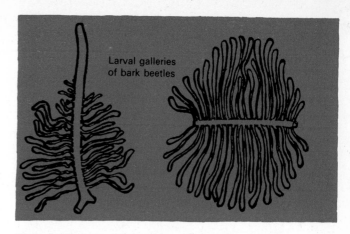

Larval galleries of bark beetles

The children could also discuss possible ways of working out the weight of food eaten by various minibeasts.

Investigating behaviour
A note here for teachers.

There are difficulties in interpreting animal behaviour. Young children are invariably anthropomorphic: they interpret animal behaviour in terms of their own feelings. We might profitably help them towards greater objectivity:

a. By concentrating on what they can observe and leave *explanations* of their observation to a later stage.

b. By discussing with them any spontaneous interpretations the children make. Almost invariably they will use a circular argument of the kind. 'It runs away because it's frightened. It's frightened because it runs away.' This is a sure indication that they are not yet ready to appreciate biological interpretations of animal behaviour. Yet it's worthwhile questioning their statements, as a precursor to later work.

How do minibeasts find their food?

Do they recognise it by: appearance?
                          smell?
                          texture?
                          taste?

Here's opportunity for investigating the senses of minibeasts. Can they see, hear, etc?

This is what Charles Darwin wrote in 1881.*

'In worms the sense of smell apparently is confined to the perception of certain odours and is feeble. They were quite indifferent to my breath as long as I breathed on them very gently . . . They exhibited the same indifference to my breath whilst I chewed some tobacco, and while a pellet of cotton wool, with a few drops of millefleurs perfume . . . was kept in my mouth.'

What a picture this conjures up! An eminent scientist huffing on worms! Children will delight in much of Darwin's writing. They might find out more about this great man of science and could profitably repeat some of his investigations. For example:

'They took not the least notice of the shrill notes from a metal whistle . . . nor did they of the deepest and loudest tones of a bassoon . . . When placed on a table close to the keys of a piano, which was played as loudly as possible, they remained perfectly quiet.

'When the pots containing two worms which had remained indifferent to the sound of the piano were placed on this instrument, and the note C in the base clef was struck, both instantly retreated into their burrows.'

Can children devise other experiments to find out if worms can hear?

Can they find out if worms can see?

Children can gain much from contact with the writings of scientists who have investigated minibeasts. Darwin and Hooke, mentioned on page 47, are good examples.

They might also learn something of Leeuwenhoek, a Dutchman who in the seventeenth century studied, among other things, the small animals in water troughs. He used a home-made microscope. Perhaps the children could make a simple microscope for their own observations. Above is one constructed by a ten-year-old which makes use of a toy magnifying glass.

Bulldog clip (moved up and down to focus)

Pocket magnifier

Handbag mirror held in place by tack

Drops of water containing minibeasts

Thin piece of glass

Building block support

Jean Henri Fabre is another scientist worth knowing about. He was a Frenchman who died in 1915. Among other things Fabre puzzled how the cabbage butterfly 'knows' where to lay her eggs so that the caterpillars will have the right kind of food.*

'Now, except when metamorphosis is at hand, the caterpillar of the White Butterfly never travels: he does all his growing on the identical plant whereon he saw the light . . . How does she (the butterfly) know her way round her botanical domain? . . . The butterfly, a nectar drinker, makes not the least enquiry into the savoury qualities of the leafage . . . This means of investigation moreover would be of no use to her, for the plant selected for the establishing of her family is for the most part not in flower.'

Is it true that the eggs are laid when the cabbages are for the most part not in flower?
Can the eggs be found on other plants?

*J. H. Fabre, 'The Cabbage Caterpillar' from The Life of Caterpillars. All Fabre's books contain a number of investigations that could be used by children.

*C. Darwin, On Humus and Earthworms.

Will caterpillars transferred to other leaves feed?
If eggs from a cabbage leaf are transferred to other leaves will the larvae develop and feed?

All kinds of profitable investigations can develop when we ask questions about the habits of the animals we observe.

In relation to feeding children might observe insect visitors to various coloured flowers. Is any colour more 'popular' than the others? Do different minibeasts visit different-coloured flowers? Can animals distinguish colour?

The children might try putting outside small dishes of sugar solution on different-coloured backgrounds. Are some dishes more popular than others? Is it a 'fair' test?

If they offer, say slugs, identical food in equally accessible bowls of different colours do the animals 'go for' particular colours?

Which foods do minibeasts 'prefer'?

At a simple level children could give their animals a choice of food. Snails, worms, caterpillars and ants make good subjects. They could provide them with a range of foodstuffs.

For example: different leaves
different fruits
meat
sweets!

Which foods are eaten?

If children discover a food preference they could perhaps try to account for it.

Perhaps food is 'chosen' because of its particular shape.
What happens if they supply different foods each with the same shape?
Identical squares of different leaves could be used.

Perhaps it's the smell that matters.
What happens if the chosen food is disguised by a strong perfume?

choice of Food

We put 22 slugs and 1 snail in a meatal tray with some food. This is their selection of food. We observed after a few minutes.

Type of food chosen	Number of creatures on it.
Rhubarb leaf	3
Potato leaf	3
Currant leaf	6
Apple leaf	1 Snail
Dock leaf	1
Cabbage	7
lettuce	2

Perhaps it's the taste.
What happens if this is disguised in some way? They could do this by allowing a salt solution to dry out on the surface but will probably have other suggestions.

Perhaps it's the feel.
How can they disguise the feel of the food?

Detailed explanations of food preferences are complex as indeed is all animal behaviour. It's best to adopt the approach 'we did . . . we discovered . . . it *might* be because . . .'

Who eats who?

Many children are fascinated by grisly details of prey–predator fights in jungle animals whilst ignorant of similar drama in their own backyards. Nature 'tooth and

...s very much in evidence in the small-scale world
...beasts and dilligent observers will get occasional
...ce of this.

Undue emphasis on bloodthirsty events is out of place
with young children but children who have acquired
wide experience of the feeding of minibeasts are ready
to 'tie together' isolated observations and who eats
who is a profitable line of inquiry. They might make
various records to organise their findings, supplementing
first-hand observation with information from books.

Some might start with fun records. They could compose
minibeast menus for the animals they have encountered
and then explore the relationships between different
diets.

Others are best helped by tabulating the information
they have gathered.

Feed on plants.	Feed on animals	Feed on dead things
Millipede	Centipede	Woodlice
Earwigs	Earwigs	Rove beetle
Plant bug	Young dragonfly	Earth worm
Bean aphid	Ground beetle larva	Carrion beetle
Butterfly	Flea	Dung beetle
Snail	Tick	House fly
Slug	Mosquito	
Leaf miner		

This animal	Eats	And is eaten by

Work of this nature will help their later understanding of
the interdependence of living things.

'This is the plant my daddy grew.
This is the snail that ate the plant
my daddy grew.
This is the thrush that ate the snail
that ate the plant my daddy grew.
This is the cat that ate the thrush, that ate the snail,
that ate the plant my daddy grew.
This is the car that ran over the cat, that ate the thrush,
that ate the snail, that ate the plant
my daddy grew.'

The ten-year-old who produced this distorted parody
of 'The House that Jack Built' was certainly gaining
appreciation of food chains in nature. Her friends
contributed similar 'chains' involving other animals.

Their findings would make a good classroom frieze.

Here is another kind of writing which indicates a child
appreciating the same idea.

'The millipede like a tank rolls on,
Over leafy mountains high.
Into the battlefield he rode
Where not so long ago,
Many battles had been fought.
You might think,
What has a war to do with millipedes?
It is a fact,
Millipedes like a cabbage now and then.
Does it bear to mind where he gets it from?
As if by magic one does appear,
Without hesitation to the cabbage went he,
Suddenly from nowhere appeared,
The enemy, the gardener.'

Any consideration of who eats who will likely involve
discussion of pests. The children could find out more
about those minibeasts whose activities are detrimental
to man's interests. For example animals that:

Eat food crops.
Attack stored food.
Cause and carry disease.
Damage materials.

Local examples of such effects are likely to be available for examination, and information about other notorious types is relevant here. Worthwhile examples include:

Teredo worms.
Tsetse flies.
Colorado beetles.
Termites.

Work of this nature has strong geographical links. Don't forget also the importance of locusts as pests. 'For they covered the face of the whole earth, so that the land was darkened; and they did eat every herb of the land', Exodus 10. 15. There's scope for drama in this account.

There may also be a chance to consider minibeasts beneficial to man's interests. For example those that:

Destroy pests.
Produce useful materials—silk, honey, etc.
Pollinate food plants.

Some of Darwin's work is relevant. He investigated the prodigious activity of earthworms in mixing soil by passing it through their bodies and casting it out in a very fine state in another place. When his findings became known, worms were not surprisingly referred to as Nature's ploughs.

Make a search for worm casts. If the children find a place where there are lots of obvious casts (eg close-cut lawns) they might extend their observations:

Do all the casts have the same shape?

Are they all the same size?

Are they made at night? during the day?

How many are made in a day? a week? . . . ?

Does the weather affect the number of casts?

What weight of soil is cast at the surface?

How does the soil from the cast compare with the soil around?

The children might dig a hole about 40 cm deep and look more closely at soil.

Can they find any worm burrows?

How deep are they?

Do all worms cast soil at the surface?

Earthworms can be kept in a classroom wormery (Chapter 8) and burrowing and casting activity conveniently observed; especially if the wormery is initially filled with layers of clearly different soil.

Finally which minibeasts are eaten by people in Britain? In other countries?

Roman Recipe for Snails.
First catch your Snails. Then wipe them with a sponge and put them in salt and milk for a day. Then in milk for several days until they are nice and fat. Then fry in oil.

Colorado beetles in action

7 How do they develop?

Animal life-cycles have for a long time figured large in school Nature study, with pride of place given to insects, particularly butterflies. This is fine, for children can gain much from such studies; they are fascinated by caterpillars spinning cocoons and enthralled by butterflies emerging from seemingly lifeless material. In a sense these exciting observations are complete in themselves, yet they are also part of a wider pattern. Investigations of the life-cycles of minibeasts can help children build up general ideas about reproduction in animals that will give greater significance to isolated observations.

Some objectives to keep in mind:

Stage 1
Development of techniques for handling living things correctly.

Awareness of seasonal changes in living things.

Ability to use books for supplementing ideas or information.

Stage 2
Willingness to assume responsibility for the proper care of living things.

Awareness of sequences of change in natural phenomena.

Appreciation of the relationships of parts and wholes.

Ability to select relevant information from books or other reference material.

Breeding from eggs to adult

Most minibeast life-cycles are too long for children to observe all events from egg to adult but ladybirds are an exception. They have a life-cycle of four to five weeks and children's interest is easily maintained over this period.

Start breeding ladybirds in early May. The sexes are not easily distinguished so it's advisable to capture two pairing or keep several in a container until you see mating take place.

When you have a pair remove the upper ladybird because he may eat any eggs the female lays: then keep the female in a transparent container and, providing she is well fed on greenfly, she will lay eggs in batches.

When one batch of eggs is produced, remove her to another container. In this way several separate lots of eggs will be available for the children. Let them watch closely using a magnifying glass or microscope. They will see interesting things over a period of three to eight days.

Once the larvae hatch from the eggs, be sure to provide plenty of greenfly or they may eat each other.

Each larva will moult three times and then turn into a pupa which *should not be disturbed*. After a further four to six days an adult will emerge. Encourage observations of its colour and spots.

Here are some observations made using a small microscope:

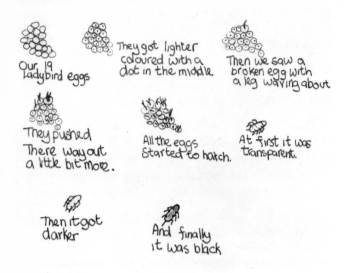

Our 19 ladybird eggs

They got lighter coloured with a dot in the middle

Then we saw a broken egg with a leg waving about

They pushed There way out a little bit more.

All the eggs started to hatch.

At first it was transparent.

Then it got darker

And finally it was black

Investigating young minibeasts

Looking at eggs

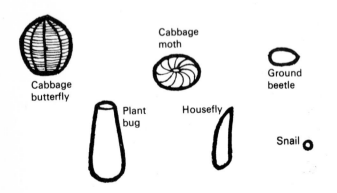

Cabbage butterfly

Cabbage moth

Ground beetle

Plant bug

Housefly

Snail

Note. Not drawn to same scale.

Go on an egg hunt

Spring to late summer is a good time to look. Explore rotting logs. Look particularly in damp crevices, at soil level, and under the bark.

Look under stones and fallen branches. Search nearby plants. Examine the undersurface of leaves and look in crevices where leaves join the stem.

Examine soil, leaf-litter and compost. Sift through the material a handful at a time and take some back to school for more detailed searching.

Children will not be able to identify many of the eggs they find. This doesn't matter. Indeed it is part of the excitement—what will they become?

Make out-door observations

Are the eggs attached to anything?

Are they easy to see—from above? from soil level?

Are they found singly or in groups? If in groups are they arranged in any particular way?

How many different kinds can the children find?

Could they make a plan of the surroundings to show where the eggs occur in order to make later visits?

How do the eggs get there? Here's opportunity to discuss mating and egg-laying.

Swallow-tailed butterflies pairing

The vast majority of minibeasts children encounter are male or female, but only a few have easily observable features making it easy to distinguish the sexes. Male and female earwigs are easily distinguishable. Perhaps the children could find information about other examples.

Some of the common minibeasts are bisexual (hermaphrodite). Worms, snails and slugs are examples. Each individual produces male and female cells and during mating an exchange of sperm takes place. Other minibeasts, aphids for example, produce young as a result of sexual mating but the females can also, under certain conditions, lay unfertilised eggs which will develop into young forms (parthenogenesis).

Make indoor observations

Collect some eggs to watch their development. Here are some general points for rearing them successfully:

1. If possible, keep then in containers with the material on which they were found, unless it is likely to decay.

2. Put them in a small escape-proof container, preferably transparent for easy observation.

3. Keep them at an even temperature in a *cool* place and wait and see what happens!

The following eggs are recommended for easy management and interest: ladybird, snail, slug, cabbage butterfly, water snails.
If eggs are difficult to obtain locally, Worldwide Butterflies and the Butterfly Farm Ltd* will supply a range with instructions for keeping them.

Also consider silkworm eggs. They will hatch readily in the classroom and the tiny caterpillars can be easily fed, ideally on mulberry leaves, but lettuce leaves will do. The caterpillars make good subjects for observation and will likely trigger off interest in silk and perhaps in other minibeasts useful to man (page 55).

Close observation of minibeast eggs will reveal fascinating things:

*See page 3.

What shape, size, colour are they? Do these change as the eggs gets older?

What's inside?

How do they compare with, say, a hen's egg?

Do all animals produce eggs?

Encourage discussion of how many are likely to hatch. Who was nearest?

Looking at larvae
A larva is essentially a growing stage in the life of an insect.

Go on a caterpillar hunt
Choose a warm sunny day in late spring or early summer and make some outdoor *observations.*

How many kinds of caterpillar can the children find?

Do any occur on more than one kind of plant?

Which are found on one particular plant only?

Do they occur in particular places on the plant?

Can anyone find a caterpillar that's not on a plant? If so, is it moving in any particular direction? If its position is changed will it change its direction?

Can anyone find a caterpillar eating?

Can anyone find signs of caterpillars feeding?

Why not make a plan of places where caterpillars are found. Will they be in the same places later in the day, the following day, next week?

Keep some caterpillars
They will need three things:

1. An escape-proof container. This should be large enough to hold adequate food and to provide places for them to pupate. It's best made of transparent material so the children can see what goes on. It should not be exposed to direct sunlight, but kept in a coolish place.

2. A supply of fresh food. Do not keep caterpillars for any length of time unless you are sure you can provide the correct food. House only those you have seen feeding out of doors or those you can identify and so find out their food requirements from books.

3. Suitable conditions for pupation. Some caterpillars pupate on their food plant, some in crevices and some in the soil. If in doubt cater for all possibilities.

Here is a suitable caterpillar cage:

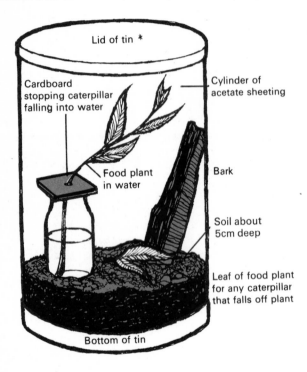

A Sellotape tin is a good size to use.

The cage is easy to maintain. Change the food plant when it shows signs of wilting. This is best done by placing a second fresh jar against the one to be removed The caterpillars can then transfer themselves, avoiding any damage caused by careless handling. Put some leaves on the soil surface for any caterpillars that fall.

If caterpillars crawl away from their food they are probably going to pupate and should not be disturbed.

Droppings should be periodically removed.

With a supply of caterpillars many interesting investigations are possible. The most obvious are those concerning movement and feeding which are discussed in Chapter 6. The following are additional suggestions:

Is there any connection between the amount of food a caterpillar eats and its growth?

Why not keep measurements of growth in length? How could changes in weight be measured?

Keep some caterpillars until they pupate and encourage close observations. Do the caterpillars travel to a special place? Do they behave in any special way?

'I think caterpillars travel to the north before they become a chrysalis.'

'Before they go off (to pupate) they move their heads round and round.'

'It (the caterpillar's movement) gets more humpety when it's going to be a chrysalis.'

Such observations invite investigation.

Investigate other larvae

Try to provide other kinds of larvae in addition to caterpillars, in order to enlarge children's experience of the range of young minibeasts. Here are some sources:

1. Shops selling fishing bait. These can provide blowfly larvae.

2. Rotting logs in spring. These will likely yield beetle and fly larvae.

3. Fungi in autumn. Split open a fleshy fungus. Careful looking may reveal 'grubs'.

4. Large plant galls. Oak "apples", thistle and rose galls are good sources. Cut one open and find a larva.

All these larva are interesting subjects for investigation and all are worth keeping to 'see what happens'. They are easy to look after.

Blowfly larvae in sawdust

Larvae in rotting logs

Larvae in fungi

Larvae in galls

Keeping a variety of larvae

Looking at pupae

This is essentially a reorganising phase in the life-cycle of an insect. It's a vulnerable stage, during which great changes result in the formation of an adult insect.

A minibeast hotel

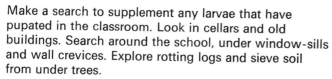

Make a search to supplement any larvae that have pupated in the classroom. Look in cellars and old buildings. Search around the school, under window-sills and wall crevices. Explore rotting logs and sieve soil from under trees.

If the pupae are attached to things do not remove them, but take the two together if possible. Soil pupae should be kept in damp (not wet) soil.

Try to keep all pupae at a cool even temperature. Here's how one class arranged its 'minibeast hotel'. Yogurt cups were bound together and anchored on

a sheltered outside window-ledge, so that the children could see into the containers through the transparent covers.

How are particular pupae protected? What's special about the covering?

How is a pupa different from the larva before it?

How does it differ from the adult it turns into?

How can various pupae be grouped? One group of girls found twelve different ways of sorting their collection into two groups.

Encourage observations of the fascinating happenings that take place when the adults emerge.

Finding out about minibeast life-cycles

Children who have collected, kept and observed many minibeasts will have gained a lot of first-hand experience which they probably supplement with information from books. They will be knowledgeable about particular animals but are unlikely to put their findings into a wider perspective.

We can help them do this if we encourage activities that lead them to consciously consider three things:

1. There is a particular sequence of events in every life-cycle.

2. There are different patterns in the life-cycles of minibeasts taken as a whole.

3. For any particular minibeast there is a strong element of chance involved in whether or not it becomes an adult.

These are statements for teachers. Suggestions for developing the ideas with children now follow.

Investigating particular life-cycles

Encourage work that gives a *visual* record of the sequence of events in the life of a particular animal. One class made a series of strip cartoons that were very popular.

In another class a group of eight-to-nine-year-olds prepared a 'film show' to tell others about a caterpillar they had been investigating. They worked together to make drawings on a long length of kitchen paper that recorded the caterpillar's birth, life and death. Their record was then rolled round a cardboard tube and put inside a carboard box having part of one side cut away. They used a second tube as a 'take-up spool' and the drawings moved slowly across the 'screen'.

As each drawing appeared someone from the group gave a commentary to the rest of the class.

This was a great success and soon other groups were producing film. Individual 'film-strips' were also made for use with a cardboard frame held in the hand.

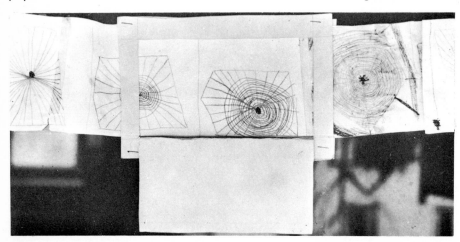

Comparing life-cycles

Here are the life-cycles of some common minibeasts.

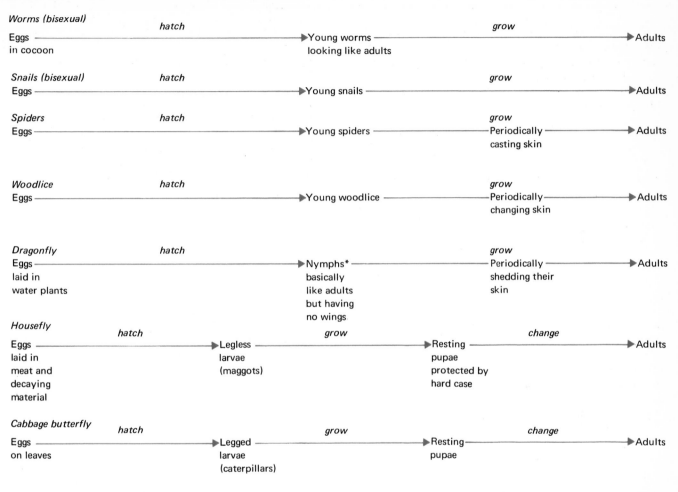

Worms (bisexual)
Eggs ——— *hatch* ——→ Young worms ——— *grow* ——→ Adults
in cocoon   looking like adults

Snails (bisexual)
Eggs ——— *hatch* ——→ Young snails ——— *grow* ——→ Adults

Spiders
Eggs ——— *hatch* ——→ Young spiders ——— *grow* ——→ Periodically casting skin ——→ Adults

Woodlice
Eggs ——— *hatch* ——→ Young woodlice ——— *grow* ——→ Periodically changing skin ——→ Adults

Dragonfly
Eggs ——— *hatch* ——→ Nymphs* basically like adults but having no wings ——— *grow* ——→ Periodically shedding their skin ——→ Adults
laid in water plants

Housefly
Eggs ——— *hatch* ——→ Legless larvae (maggots) ——— *grow* ——→ Resting pupae protected by hard case ——— *change* ——→ Adults
laid in meat and decaying material

Cabbage butterfly
Eggs ——— *hatch* ——→ Legged larvae (caterpillars) ——— *grow* ——→ Resting pupae ——— *change* ——→ Adults
on leaves

These examples are given to illustrate the range of minibeast life-cycles. In some, for example, worms, snails, woodlice, spiders, centipedes, the life-cycle is essentially:

Egg ——————→ 'Miniature adult' ——————→ Adult

In *insects* the pattern is more complex.
Some insects, for example, dragonflies and grass-hoppers, have a comparatively simple cycle:

Egg ——————→ Nymph ——————→ Adult

But most of the insect life-cycles children encounter will be of the kind:

Egg ——→ Larva ——→ Pupa ——→ Adult

Teachers aware of these differences can better help children to appreciate individual life-cycles as part of a wider pattern.

See page 83.

Encourage records that can be used to retrieve comparative information about different life-cycles. The example quoted below illustrates one possibility: there are others.

A class of top juniors had been studying minibeasts for several weeks. The children were enthusiastic about their work and it showed no sign of abating. Their teacher was aware that there was a large amount of experience and information available in the class as a whole, but that individuals were so engrossed in particular studies that they were not gaining knowledge of other people's work. He discussed the problem with the class. How could they gather together everything they had found out?

An elaborate punched card system resulted. It was designed by teacher and children working together.

Here's a copy of a card relating to life-cycles.

Animal's name _____		
Does it live on land?	YES	O
in water?		O
Does it lay eggs?	YES	O
	NO	O
Does it look after its eggs?	YES	O
	NO	O
Do the eggs hatch to look like the animal?	YES	O
	NO	O
If the eggs turn into a larva has it got legs?	YES	O
	NO	O
Does it go to a special place to become a pupa?	YES	O
	NO	O
Does the young animal live in the same place as the adult?	YES	O
	NO	O

The children used a card for each animal they had investigated, completing it by cutting the relevant hole

for each question. With a Yes answer the card looked like this:

YES
NO

When all the cards were stacked together every Yes answer for a particular question could be quickly discovered by putting a needle through the hole and collecting the cards that dropped out.

The children then made additional records, listing, for example, all the animals they found whose eggs hatched to look like the adult.

There are two important points about this particular study.

1. It arose after considerable experience of minibeasts.

2. It was developed by a particular teacher and a particular class.

Teachers might like to consider making such cards with their children but the card illustrated indicates an approach; it is not a work card to be introduced 'from cold'.

Thinking about chance
In any work on minibeast life-cycles there is an underlying theme: it's all a chancey business. And although this is something young children cannot fully understand, it is something we can help them appreciate.

Children see things in particular: that an egg becomes a caterpillar, becomes a pupa, becomes a butterfly. (Though the idea of sequence of events in life-cycles is but slowly established.) Through discussion arising from their work we might help them to see that not all eggs become caterpillars, nor do all caterpillars become pupae . . . that in general when lots of eggs are laid very few become adults. This ties in with the idea of parental care: when eggs are looked after, fewer are usually laid. Think of birds, or man.

Do the minibeasts the children find look after their young?

What dangers do young animals encounter if they are not looked after by parents?

Which animals do look after their young?
Social insects, bees, ants and wasps are relevant here. These minibeasts look after their young, though not in the parental sense known to the children. The allocation of jobs within the colony is fascinating and offers tremendous scope for investigation.

Why not visit a beekeeper? It will trigger off lots of work.

Why not find an ants' nest, and just look?

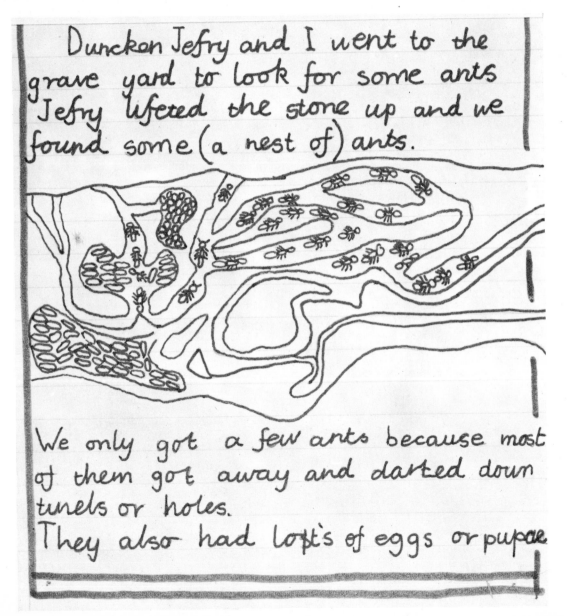

Duncken Jefry and I went to the grave yard to look for some ants Jefry lifeted the stone up and we found some (a nest of) ants.

We only got a few ants because most of them got away and darted down tunels or holes.
They also had loft's of eggs or pupae

8 How can we keep them?

Many of the minibeasts children encounter can be easily kept in classrooms, for in general they demand less attention than warm-blooded animals. This is their advantage, but against this must be set the fact that they do not engender in children the same sense of caring that more cuddly, warm, furry animals do. They are fascinating in small doses but seldom exciting enough to justify long-term keeping just for keeping's sake. Their period of stay in the classroom is best governed by their contribution to the children's work. Mostly they will be wanted for short-term observation and investigation and then returned to their natural environment. If this is the case they can be temporarily housed in any suitable container that is escape-proof. They will live happily without feeding for a few days, but land animals should have moist surroundings (damp moss or cotton wool in the container) and aquatic animals must have adequate oxygen (see page 23).

Occasionally children may want to keep minibeasts for longer periods. This is likely if the animals are:

1. Sufficiently active to generate sustained, if intermittent, interest.

2. Needed for lengthy investigations.

3. Kept in order that their complete life-cycle can be seen.

In these cases they require more permanent housing and maintenance.

It is not possible to give details for *all* animals. Those listed are commonly found, easy to cope with and profitable subjects for observation and investigation. The suggestions are given as guidance for teachers, but do involve the children in planning how they will keep their minibeasts. Encourage them to devise and design suitable accommodation since this provides a problem-solving situation that will promote wider experience than just making use of particular apparatus.

With young children it's best achieved through discussion along the lines . . . What will the animal need? . . . How shall we make sure it has these things? Older children might be given written guidance that encourages independent work.

Here's a duplicated sheet made for top juniors. It was used frequently at various times when different animals were collected and brought into the classroom.

KEEPING ANIMALS IN SCHOOL

Use your own knowledge and books to answer these questions.

1. What is it called?

2. Where did you find it?

3. What does it eat?

4. Does it need water to drink?

5. How did you find out the answers to questions 3 and 4?

6. Can you get a supply of food for it?

7. Did you find it in a damp or dry place?

8. Was it in the light or in the dark?

9. Is the animal adult? If it is not, will it need special conditions to change to an adult?

10. How did you find out the answers to questions 8 and 9?

11. Watch it moving. Will you have to make a special structure so that it can move freely?

Use your answers to these questions, to plan some housing for your animal. Make a drawing of your ideas and we'll discuss them.

Some objectives to keep in mind:

Stage 1
Sensitivity to the need for giving proper care to living things.

Skill in manipulating tools and materials.

Ability to use books for supplementing ideas or information.

Development of a concept of environment.

Stage 2
Enjoyment in developing methods for solving problems or testing ideas.

Skill in devising and constructing simple apparatus.

Ability to select relevant information from books or other reference material.

Appreciation of interdependence among living things.

Keeping animals in the classroom

Land animals
The details given below apply to adult minibeasts. You will find guidance in Chapter 7 about keeping eggs, larvae and pupae. For easy reference the animals are listed in alphabetical order.

Ants

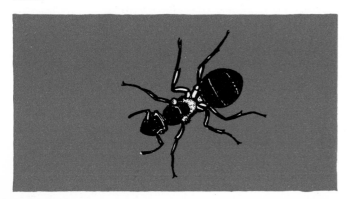

Temporary housing

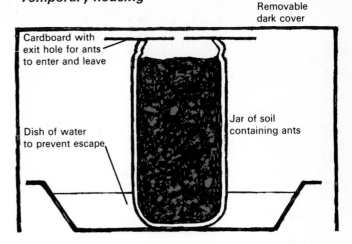

Removable dark cover

Cardboard with exit hole for ants to enter and leave

Dish of water to prevent escape

Jar of soil containing ants

Feeding
Cotton wool soaked sugar solution can be placed on the cardboard.

More permanent housing
Ants' nests with their queen can be kept in sweet bottles, or in soil between glass plates as in the wormery (page 90). The soil must be kept damp and a blackout provided.

Ants may also be kept in formicaria especially constructed for the purpose.

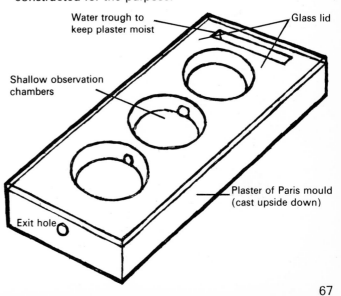

Water trough to keep plaster moist

Glass lid

Shallow observation chambers

Plaster of Paris mould (cast upside down)

Exit hole

Aphids

Flies

Blow-flies are easy to rear from their maggots (page 61) and can be kept for observation in jars.

Note. Winged forms also occur.

Aphids will thrive and multiply providing they have adequate food. Bean aphids can be reared on plants grown specially for the purpose or on renewable food-stuff obtained from outside. Wingless forms will remain on the food plant but winged forms must be contained. The caterpillar cage shown on page 60 is suitable. Aphids are most exciting when kept in association with other animals. Ladybirds could be introduced to feed on the aphids.

Aphids can also be kept in association with ants. Below is a system devised by some ten-year-olds.

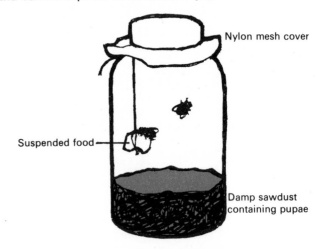

Nylon mesh cover

Suspended food

Damp sawdust containing pupae

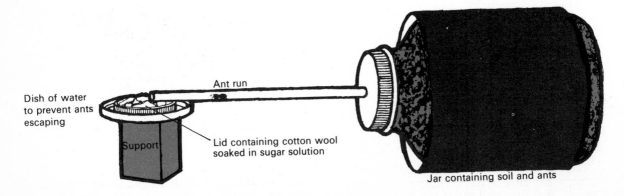

Dish of water to prevent ants escaping

Ant run

Support

Lid containing cotton wool soaked in sugar solution

Jar containing soil and ants

Feeding

Try small pieces of meat introduced on a length of cotton for easy removal. It is best to change the meat every day or so to prevent an offensive smell, but make sure the flies have had a meal; they have to make the meat liquid and then suck it up. They can also be given cotton wool soaked in honey, or sugar solution.

When removing the cover, you can prevent flies escaping by first chilling the jar in a refrigerator until they are inactive. In the interests of hygiene it's a good idea to wrap the container in foil or a polythene bag before putting it in the fridge.

Ladybirds and other beetles

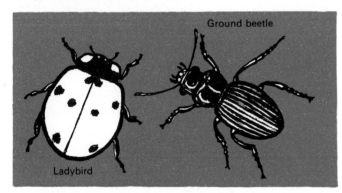

Ground beetle

Ladybird

Ladybirds are easy to keep in any container that allows them room to fly. They must feed on live aphids. These are best supplied by introducing aphid-infested plants (rose, bean, for example) into the container.

Plant-feeding or scavenging beetles are also easy to keep. Any escape-proof container providing damp conditions is suitable.

Millipedes

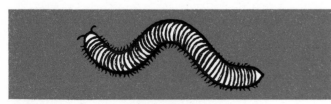

Millipedes can be kept in damp earth and fed on soft green leaves or pieces of fruit. (Centipedes are not so convenient to keep because they are carnivorous.)

Slugs

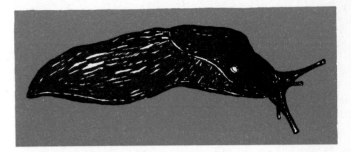

Slugs thrive best in dark damp surroundings from which they can be removed for observation.

Suitable housing

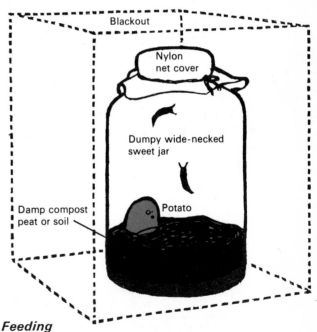

Blackout

Nylon net cover

Dumpy wide-necked sweet jar

Damp compost peat or soil

Potato

Feeding

Non-messy vegetable material whose remains can be easily removed, eg half an apple, potato.

Maintenance

Keep surroundings moist. Slugs in captivity are prone to infestation by tiny white mites and they should be cleaned out regularly. After about a fortnight remove the compost (isolate any eggs) and add fresh material to the washed-out jar. Before transferring slugs to their fresh surroundings, roll them in blotting paper to remove surplus mucus.

Snails

Requirements
Secure transparent container. Damp surroundings, some shelter, soil in which to lay eggs.

Suitable housing
Small-scale keeping : Large jam jars or refrigerator boxes. Class snailery : An aquatic tank is very convenient. A less expensive and easily stored large container can be made from glass plates and wood. Details for its construction are outlined at the end of Chapter 10.

Feeding
Food is best added in one place so that uneaten material can be easily removed—a plastic lid sunk into the soil is good. Snails are best fed on oats rolled in crushed chalk. This diet will keep them healthy and their droppings will be firm and easily removed. They will, of course, eat most garden produce but this results in messy droppings with consequent cleaning difficulties.

Maintenance
Remove droppings periodically. Sprinkle soil with water to keep it moist. If the snailery becomes too dry the snails will become inactive and form a covering at the mouth of their shell (the epiphragm). If this happens

their activity can be restored by *gently* running *warm* water over their shell.

Dismantle occasionally, search for eggs which can be isolated and reared separately in small containers.

Spiders

Most spiders can be kept successfully for a few weeks without feeding, but will die quickly without water. They can be kept in jars with a shallow container of water which must be frequently renewed. They can be fed on flies. The house spider and garden spider will spin webs in captivity if they have enough space to do so and suitable supports for the web.

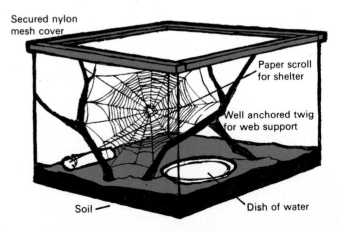

Secured nylon mesh cover

Paper scroll for shelter

Well anchored twig for web support

Soil

Dish of water

Woodlice

Note. There are several kinds of woodlice distinguished by such things as the nature of the antennae, the nature of the tail end. Only one kind, the pill woodlouse, rolls up into a ball.

Requirements
Damp surroundings, some shelter.

Suitable housing

Bark for shelter

Lining of damp blotting paper

Flat dish with perforated cover of nylon mesh or polythene

Maintenance
Clean out and renew when the blotting paper gets tatty.

Worms

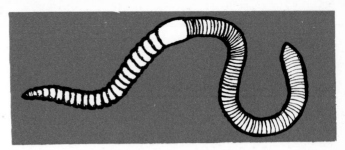

Note. There are a number of different earthworms distinguished by such things as: colour of body, colour of clitellum, position of clitellum, number of segments, shape of tail.

Requirements
Damp dark surroundings. Soil in which to burrow. This is best taken from place where worms were collected, but avoid heavy clay.

Suitable housing
Transparent containers with removable 'blackout' on a small scale, jam jars with black paper covers are suitable.

For a class-scale wormery see details at the end of Chapter 10.

Feeding

Not required frequently if the soil is 'rich'. Occasional addition of leaves or compost at the surface is helpful.

Maintenance

Don't let the soil dry out or get waterlogged. An occasional sprinkling will keep it moist. Dismantle wormeries periodically and search for worm capsules (hardish, brownish, about 2 mm long). The capsules can be isolated to develop in small containers lined with damp moss or damp blotting paper.

Water animals

Setting up an aquarium

1. Select a suitable container

This is one that will give a large surface of water in relation to its volume. Commercially produced aquaria are excellent because of the high visibility they provide. Washing-up bowls arranged so that children can look down on the inhabitants are much cheaper if less adequate.

2. Obtain the bottom material

Silver sand from horticultural shops is best (seashore sand will not do because it is too salty). Wash the sand well to remove dust and then arrange it in the container to a depth of about 4 cm. Add a few well-washed stones for visual effect and to provide shelter for the animals.

3. Add water

Tap water is normally quite adequate if not heavily chlorinated. It is advisable to use water that has been standing overnight. Children will, of course, be involved in setting up the aquarium, and it is useful to ask them to estimate how much water they will need: a good experience of capacity.

To avoid disrupting the bottom material it is useful to pour the water on to a piece of card which will break the water force and float upwards as the container fills up. Do not overfill: fill to about two-thirds of the depth and allow a high surface/volume ratio.

It's useful to mark the level of the water since later observations will show some has 'disappeared', and may lead to profitable investigations.

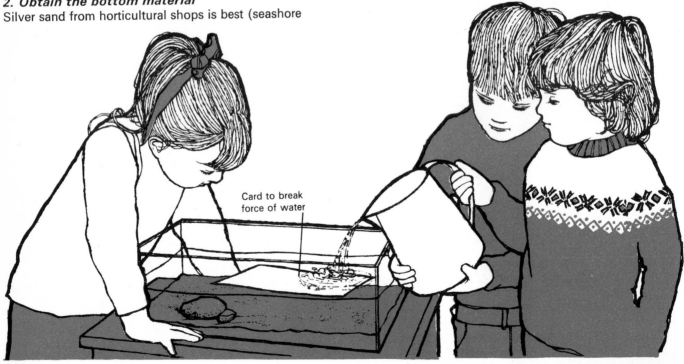

Card to break force of water

4. Add some plants

If collected from ponds these should be well washed. Try to provide a variety of growth.

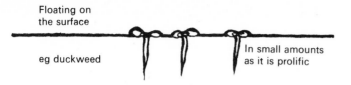

Floating on the surface

eg duckweed

In small amounts as it is prolific

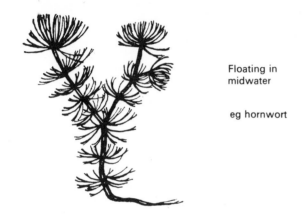

Floating in midwater

eg hornwort

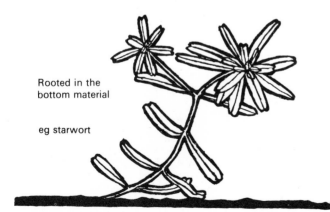

Rooted in the bottom material

eg starwort

5. Add some animals

Unless special arrangements are made to aerate the aquarium, these must be animals from still water. Take care to choose animals that will live well together and not eat each other. Here are some:

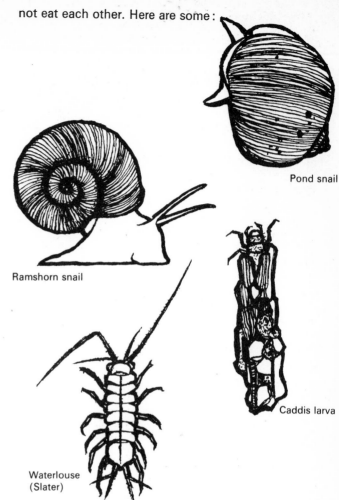

Pond snail

Ramshorn snail

Caddis larva

Waterlouse (Slater)

Goldfish might be added for additional interest. These should be obtained from reputable dealers and if fish-keeping is a new venture, select the goldiest. Dappled colouration is attractive but it may indicate disease. The fish will need food which can be obtained from a pet shop.

6. Add a cover

This keeps out dust. Stand the container in a convenient place. Do not keep it in direct sunlight.

A well-balanced aquarium will need little maintenance, apart from topping up. Should the water become murky, try adding more snails or reducing the light.

Keeping isolated pond animals

Some pond animals are voracious feeders on other animals and best kept separately. They include:

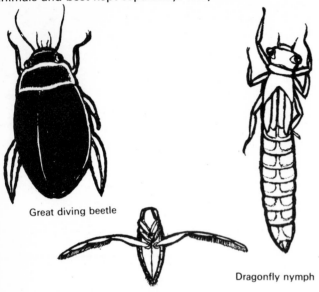

Great diving beetle

Dragonfly nymph

Water boatman

They can be housed in covered 'mini aquaria', in jars, pie dishes, etc, and are best fed on raw meat, suspended in the water by cotton so that uneaten portions can be easily removed. Dragonfly nymphs will need some means of escape from the water when they are ready to emerge as adults.

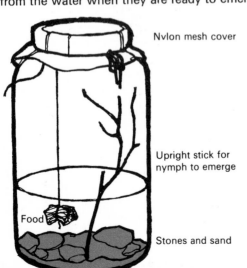

Nylon mesh cover

Upright stick for nymph to emerge

Food

Stones and sand

Keeping the school surroundings well stocked

Some suggestions follow for enriching the minibeast population within the school grounds. Clearly these are long-term ploys, but once established they can lead to all kinds of exciting discoveries.

Lay old sacks in a little-used corner.

Old sacks encourage minibeasts

Establish a compost heap.

Introduce some rotting logs.

Allow a small area of any grass to 'run wild' and stay 'wild'.

Similarly keep part of any flower border or hedge permanently 'wild'.

Grow flowers in tubs or borders that will encourage a range of insect visitors. Include a range of flower shape and colour.

Set up ventilation bricks in a sunny sheltered spot with the cavities lined with paper tubes to encourage certain bees and wasps.

Use old sinks to collect rainwater and see what animal life becomes established.

Consider making a pond. You will find instructions in many books about water gardening. Miminal details are given here:

1. Dig a large hole.

2. Line it with heavy-duty polythene anchored at the side with stones or cement. It is useful to build up the sides a little to prevent too much soil washing into the water.

3. Add soil and gravel (taking care not to puncture the polythene) as bottom material.

4. Establish some water plants.

5. Add water.

If you make plans for increasing the stock of minibeasts around the school, do discuss possibilities with the children. Talking about getting more minibeasts

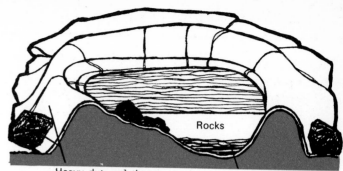

Rocks

Heavy-duty polythene anchored by stones or cement

Bottom material

inevitably involves considering the kind of conditions animals 'prefer' and further discussion will likely promote investigation.

In one school it led to a group of boys designing an experiment to see which one of a number of varyingly combined conditions encouraged most minibeasts.

It's a fitting example to end the suggestions for children's activities in this book, because, in their handling of the variables of the situation, they showed themselves to be approaching Stage 3.

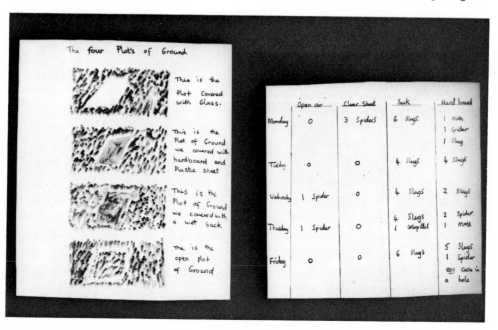

The four Plots of Ground

This is the Plot Covered with Glass.

This is the Plot of Ground we covered with hardboard and Plastic sheet

This is the Plot of Ground we covered with a wet Sack

This is the open plot of Ground

	Open air	Clear Sheet	Sack	Hard board
Monday	0	3 Spiders	6 Slugs	1 moth, 1 Spider, 1 Slug
Tuesday	0	0	4 Slugs	4 Slugs
Wednesday	1 Spider	0	4 Slugs	2 Slugs
Thursday	1 Spider	0	4 Slugs, 1 caterpillar	2 Spider, 1 moth
Friday	0	0	6 Slugs	5 Slugs, 1 Spider, egg case in a hole

9 Identification guide lines for teachers

Scheme for common land animals

The following scheme indicates things to look for which will place common animals in groups based on a pattern of animal classification.

It will not identify all animals but it will help non-specialists make comment on the children's finds and will facilitate further identification from reference books (see Bibliography).

There are two points to note about the scheme:

1. It is restricted to animals that can easily be seen with the naked eye. *

2. Its diagrams indicate the main features of particular animals, but they are not all drawn to the same scale.

First decision for identifying common land animals

Has the animal got legs?

No   go to Chart A, 'Common legless minibeasts'.

Yes go to Chart B, 'Common minibeasts with legs'.

Smaller animals are included in the Nuffield Foundation keys to small organisms in soil, litter and water troughs. See Bibliography for details.

Chart A   Common legless minibeasts

Animal has a shell	Animal has no shell	
Snails of all kinds	**Body is not segmented**	**Body is segmented**

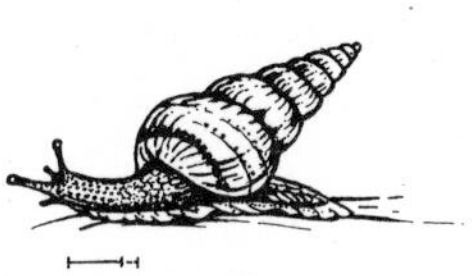

Animal has a shell

Snails of all kinds

H. 15-26 mm

Shell B. 5·5-7 mm

H. 12-23 mm

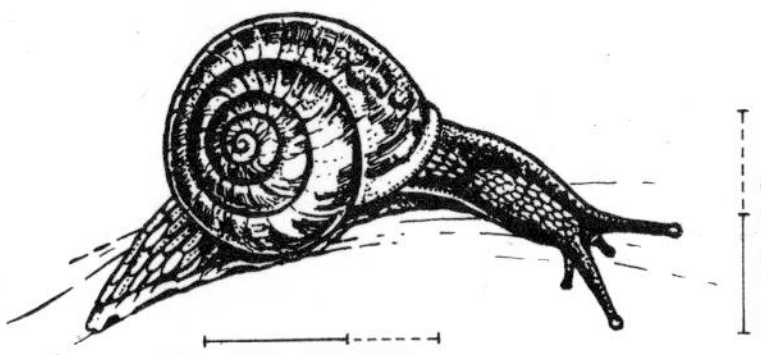

Shell B. 15-25 mm

Body is not segmented

Various slugs

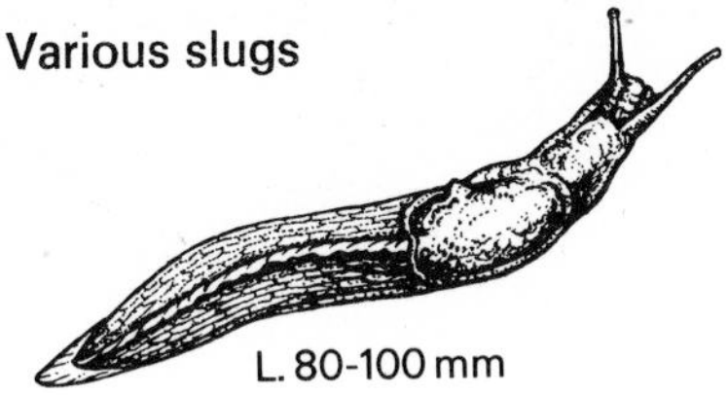

L. 80-100 mm

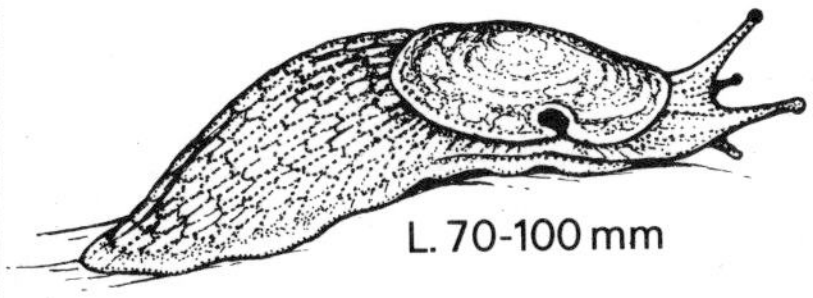

L. 70-100 mm

See key on page 41

Body is segmented

Worms

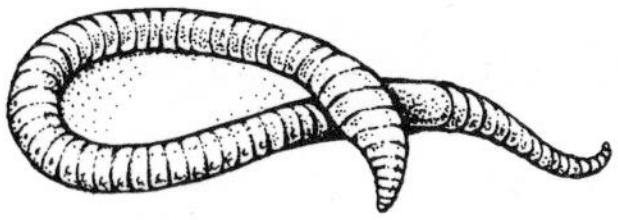

L. 120 mm

Immature insects
Larvae

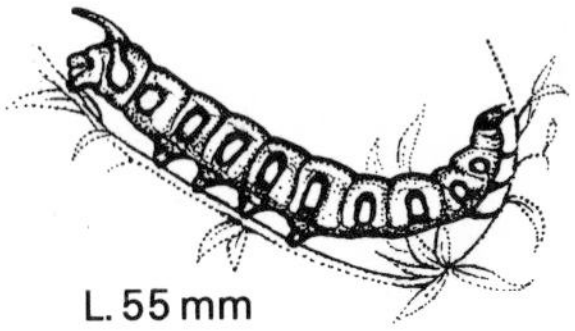

L. 55 mm

Pupae

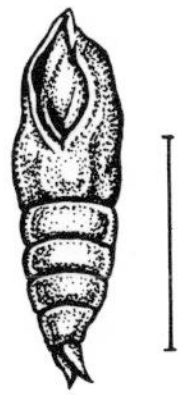

22 mm

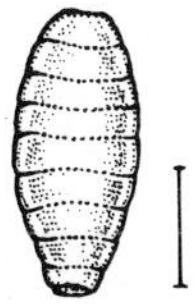

12 mm

Go to Chart G

Chart B   Common minibeasts with legs

Animal has many legs	Animal has four pairs of legs	Animal has three pairs of legs
Less than twelve pairs Woodlice 15 mm *See page 71*	*Body in two parts* Spiders Trap-door spider × 2	*Insects* See opposite page
More than twelve pairs One pair of legs on each segment: Centipedes 47 mm Two pairs of legs on each segment: Millipedes 30 mm	*Body in one part* Harvest-men Harvest-man × 1⅓	

Identifying insects

There are so many different kinds of insects that it is impossible to give a single handy scheme catering for all types.

The following guide lines indicate things to look for that will help with the recognition of commoner types and also aid further identification.

Has it wings? If so how many?
Wing features will enable you to start your identification.

Other observations that will help subsequent identification include:

What is the wing texture?
What are the relative sizes of the wings?
Have the wings many veins or few?
Has the body a characteristic shape?
Have the antennae any special features?
Are there special features at the tip of the abdomen?

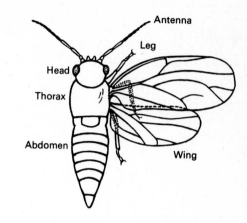

Simplified representation of insect structure

First decision for identifying insects

Has it got wings, and if so, how many?

Two pairs of obvious wings	go to	Chart C
Two pairs of wings but one pair *hidden* under hard wing-cases*	go to	Chart D
One pair of wings only	go to	Chart E
No wings	go to	Chart F

*Note. *Some insects have two pairs of wings but this is not easily seen unless the animal is in flight. Their membranous wings are hidden under hard wing-cases.*

Chart C   Common insects with two pairs of obvious wings

All wings are scaly	Wings are neither hairy nor scaly
Antennae are slender and knobbed Butterflies	**Both wings are about the same size**

Long and narrow

Eyes touching

Dragonflies ×⁵⁄₆

Eyes not touching

Damselflies ×1⅓

Not long and narrow

eg Lacewings ×1⅓

×1⅓

Antennae not knobbed

Moths

Forewings are larger than hindwings

Wings have few veins

Body has waist

Wasps, also bees, ants ×²⁄₃

Body has no waist

Sawflies ×1⅓

Wings have many veins

Wings are hairy

Caddis flies ×⁵⁄₆

Mayflies, also grasshoppers, aphids ×⁸⁄₉

Chart D Insects with membranous wings hidden under hard wing-case

| **Animal has characteristic shield-shaped part (scutellum) on its back** | **Animal has no scutellum** |

Animal has characteristic shield-shaped part (scutellum) on its back

Land bugs

eg Froghoppers, capsid bugs, shield bugs

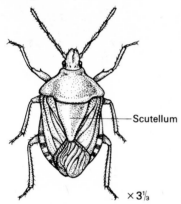

×3⅓

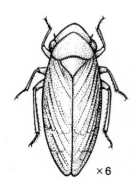

×6

Animal has no scutellum

Wing-cases are shorter than body

Pincers at end of abdomen

eg Earwigs

No pincers

Rove-beetles

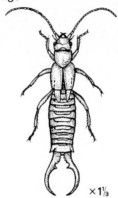

×1⅓

×3⅓

Wing-cases are almost as long as body

Beetles : for example

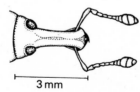

With snout
Weevils

3 mm

Sawedged antennae
Click-beetles

×10

Plated antennae
Dung-beetles

×7⅓

Chart E Common insects with only one pair of wings

Insect has fragile body and long antennae	Insect has stumpy body and short antennae
Craneflies ×1⅓	*Various short-horned flies, for example:*
	Housefly ×2⅔
Midges Mosquitoes ×2⅔	Horsefly ×2
	Robberfly ×2

Chart F Common insects with no wings

Nymphs*

Grasshopper nymph

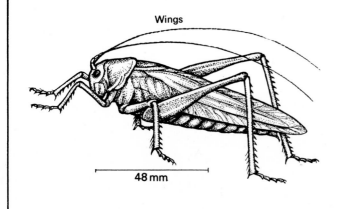

Wing buds

16 mm

Adult grasshopper

Wings

48 mm

Nymphs have the same features as the adult form except that their wing develops gradually. Young nymphs may therefore appear to be wingless, but close examination will likely show the presence of wing buds.

Adult insects

These include: tiny insects that are always wingless

eg Silverfish, bristletails, springtails

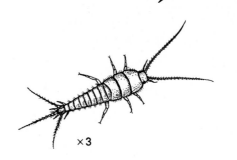

×10

×3

Also: the wingless forms of other winged insects

eg Ants, aphids

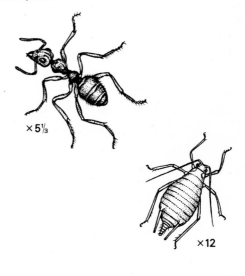

×5⅓

×12

Chart G   Common insects with no wings

Immature insects	
Larvae	**Pupae**

Larvae

Larvae is legless

Fly larvae (maggots)

×2

Larvae has three pairs of legs

Beetle larvae

×2

×2

Larvae has three pairs of legs and other
structures functioning as legs (false legs)

Two pairs of false legs:
Looper caterpillars of moths

×²/₃

Five pairs of false legs:
Caterpillars of butterflies
and moths

×⅓

More than five pairs of false legs:
Sawfly larvae

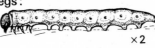

×2

Pupae

Pupa has free legs

Some beetles, sawflies

×1⅓

Pupa has legs visible but not free

Butterflies and moths

×1⅓

Pupa is legless

Short-horned flies

×1⅓

The classification of common minibeasts

The identification guide lines in this chapter have been constructed so that common animals can be 'pigeon-holed' by non-specialists. Technical names have been avoided, but as these may assist further identification and reading they are included in the following classification of small animals which indicates the pattern of the groupings mentioned.

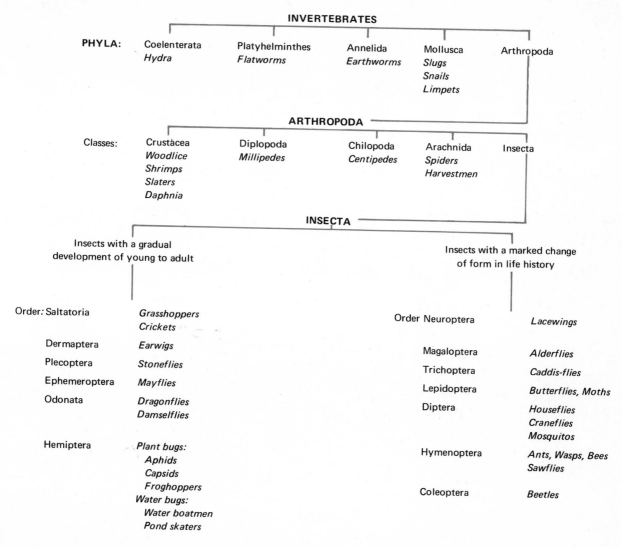

INVERTEBRATES

PHYLA:

Coelenterata	Platyhelminthes	Annelida	Mollusca	Arthropoda
Hydra	*Flatworms*	*Earthworms*	*Slugs*	
			Snails	
			Limpets	

ARTHROPODA

Classes:

Crustàcea	Diplopoda	Chilopoda	Arachnida	Insecta
Woodlice	*Millipedes*	*Centipedes*	*Spiders*	
Shrimps			*Harvestmen*	
Slaters				
Daphnia				

INSECTA

Insects with a gradual development of young to adult

Insects with a marked change of form in life history

Order: Saltatoria	*Grasshoppers*
	Crickets
Dermaptera	*Earwigs*
Plecoptera	*Stoneflies*
Ephemeroptera	*Mayflies*
Odonata	*Dragonflies*
	Damselflies
Hemiptera	*Plant bugs:*
	Aphids
	Capsids
	Froghoppers
	Water bugs:
	Water boatmen
	Pond skaters

Order Neuroptera	*Lacewings*
Magaloptera	*Alderflies*
Trichoptera	*Caddis-flies*
Lepidoptera	*Butterflies, Moths*
Diptera	*Houseflies*
	Craneflies
	Mosquitos
Hymenoptera	*Ants, Wasps, Bees*
	Sawflies
Coleoptera	*Beetles*

Key to common pond animals

1.	Has it shell?	Yes go to	2
		No go to	3
2.	What is the shape of the shell?	Raised coil =	Pond snail
		Flat coil =	Ramshorn snail
3.	Is the body made up of different sections?	Yes go to	4
		No =	Flatworm
4.	Has it legs?	Yes go to	5
		No go to	20
5.	How many legs?	Three pairs go to	6
		Four pairs go to	19
		More than four pairs =	Water louse
6.	Has it wings? Look carefully!	Yes go to	7
		No go to	15
7.	Can you see antennae?	Yes go to	8
		No go to	13
8.	What shape are the antennae?	Thread-like go to	9
		Club-like go to	10
		Thin and as long as the first pair of legs go to	11
9.	How long is it?	Longer than 25 mm =	Carnivorous water beetle
		Less than 25 mm =	Other water beetle, eg Agabus
10.	How long is it?	Longer than 25 mm =	Silver water beetle
		Less than 25 mm =	Whirligig beetle
11.	Look carefully at the head. Is it much longer than it is broad?	Yes =	Water-measurer
		No go to	12
12.	Look at legs 1 and 2 (1 is nearest head) Are they widely separated?	Yes =	Pond-skater
		No =	Water cricket
13.	Has it a tail tube?	Yes =	Water scorpion
		No go to	14

Key to common pond animals

14.	Which way up does the animal swim ?	On back	=	Water boatman
		On front	=	Corixid
15.	Does it live in a tube ?	Yes	=	Caddis larva
		No	go to	16
16.	Has it tail projections ?	Yes	go to	17
		No	=	Whirligig larva
17.	How many tail projections ?	Two	=	Dysticus larva
		Three	go to	18
18.	What shape are the projections ?	Long and thin	=	Mayfly nymph
		Long flat plates	=	Damselfly nymph
		Short and stumpy	=	Dragonfly nymph
19.	How long is it ?	Less than 5 mm long	=	Water mite
		More than 5 mm long	=	Water spider
20.	Has it antennae ?	No	go to	21
		Yes	go to	22
21.	Has it suckers ?	Yes	=	Leech
		No	=	Fresh water worm
22.	Has it a breathing tube at the back ?	Yes	=	Mosquito, gnat larvae
		No	go to	23
23.	Is its body transparent ?	Yes	=	Midge larvae
		No (red)	=	Bloodworm

10 Useful materials and equipment

In this short chapter we will collect together the materials and equipment commonly mentioned in the text, since many teachers find it useful to have an over-all picture of likely needs before embarking on particular work with children.

Things for outdoor observation and collection

Things recommended for each child or small group

Convenient-sized hardboard (20 x 30 cm) with paper and pencil attached for outdoor recording. It's a good idea to keep this in a polythene bag in case of rain.

A paintbrush and plastic teaspoon for moving minibeasts to containers.

Two small screw-topped containers. These are often obtainable from chemists free of charge.

A small polythene bag.

For collecting minibeasts from water extra items are needed:

A plastic kitchen strainer.

A flat dish—preferably light coloured.

A plastic tea-strainer.

Things recommended for a central supply

Polythene bags of varying sizes.

A collection of screw-topped containers.

Measuring tapes.

A few pooters (page 24).

A few nature viewers. These can be obtained from World-wide Butterflies Ltd, Overcompton, Sherborne, Dorset.

Buckets.

A trowel.

For water explorations a long-handled pond net is useful and its advisable to take an old towel.

In any expedition away from school it's also advisable to include a simple first-aid kit.

Things for work in the classroom

Nature viewers.

A simple binocular microscope of the Bausch and Lomb type.

Varied surfaces. 30×30 cm is a convenient size. Include polystyrene, cardboard, corrugated paper, metal, glass, polythene, wood, plastic foam, fabrics of various kinds.

Simple timing and measuring devices.

Miscellaneous items such as string, cotton, adhesives.

Simple tools and materials for constructing apparatus.

Constructional details for a classroom wormery and snailery

Classroom snailery
Suitable also for other land invertebrates.

1.2 cm × 1.2 cm wooden frame

Wooden retaining strip

Base board

Glass

Cover

15 cm

40 cm

70 cm

Corners glued and screwed

Polythene

Adhesive tape

The snailery described is cheap, very easy to assemble and is collapsible for convenient transport and storage.

Note. Dimensions can be varied to suit individual preference.

Assembly
1. Obtain the baseboard (plywood or hardboard). Varnish with a couple of coats of clear polyurethane.

2. Obtain the glass (4 mm thickness is good). Clean and dry thoroughly.

3. Position the glass vertically on the baseboard (it can be temporarily held in place with Sellotape). Mark the outside edge of the glass to correspond with the inside edge of the three retaining wood strips.

4. Tack or glue (Evo-stik Woodworking adhesive is good) the wood strips in place, along the marked lines.

5. When in use the glass is secured at the corners by adhesive tape positioned within the three retaining wood strips.

Additional tape on the exposed edges is a good safety precaution.

When not required the corner tape is removed and the whole structure stored flat.

6. Construct the cover.
Make a rectangular frame from 1.2 × 1.2 cm wood to just fit outside the glass walls. (The frame can be glued together with Evo-stik and then screwed at the corners for additional strength.)

Now cover the frame with strong transparent polythene glued to the frame strips (Bostik No. 1 is adequate).

Classroom wormery

Note. Dimensions can be varied to suit individual preference.

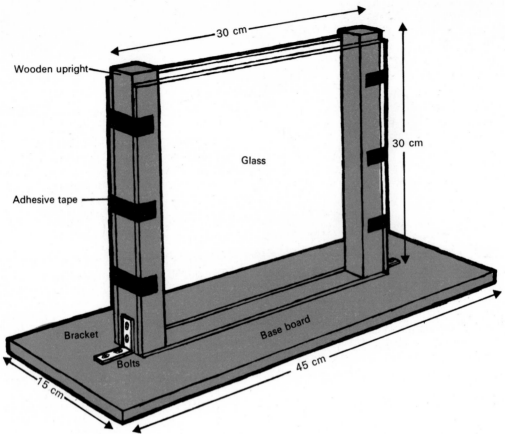

Construction details

Obtain:
Baseboard (plywood is good).
Two pieces of 4 mm glass.
Two wooden uprights.
Two corner brackets (steel 7.5 × 7.5 cm right-angle brackets are best).

1. Varnish baseboard and uprights (aerosol varnish is easiest to use but more expensive than the brush-on variety).

2. Screw brackets to wooden uprights.

3. Hold glass and uprights in position on baseboard. Mark in position of retaining bolts on the baseboard.

4. Bolt brackets to baseboard (can be screwed if flat storage is not required).

5. For class use, place glass against uprights and anchor with adhesive tape.

6. Fill with soil (see page 71) and add a removable light-proof cover.

Bibliography

Books for teachers

The following selection of books may be helpful to teachers. (Those marked with an asterisk also have classroom use.)

Dale, A., *Patterns of Life*, Heinemann.
A general nature study book including information about the structure and life-history of common minibeasts.

Lulham, R., *Introduction to Zoology through Nature Study*, Macmillan.
A general book about invertebrates arranged on a basis of scientific classification. Its style and format are rather outdated but it contains a wealth of valuable information.

Savory, T. H., *The World of Small Animals*, University of London Press.
A good general book surveying a number of invertebrate groups to encourage 'amateur-specialisation'.

*Stanek, V. J., *Pictorial Encyclopedia of the Animal Kingdom*, Hamlyn.
A book of stimulating photographs (mostly black and white); roughly one-fifth devoted to minibeasts.

Friedlander, C. P., and Priest, D. A., *Insects and Spiders*, Pitman.
Primarily an identification book containing a number of keys (technical terms defined). Black and white line diagrams.

Oldroyd, H., *Insects and their World*, British Museum Publications.
An informative survey of insects.

*Blandford Colour Series: *Field and Meadow Life, Woodland Life, Pond and Stream Life, Insects in Colour.* Each book in two sections. The first contains excellent colour illustrations of a comprehensive range of minibeasts that can be enjoyed by teachers and children of all ages; the second has supplementary information useful to teachers.*

*Young Specialist Series:
Pond Life, Molluscs, Butterflies and Moths, Burke.
Teachers and able top juniors.

Warne Series:
Step, E. S., *Bees, Wasps, Ants and Allied Insects of the British Isles.*
Step, E. S., *Shell Life.*
South, R., *Butterflies of the British Isles.*
South, R., *Moths of the British Isles.*
Savory, T. H., *Spiders and Allied Orders of the British Isles.*
Savory, T. H., *The Spider's Web.*
Longfield, C., *Dragonflies of the British Isles.*
Stokoe, W. J. (compiler), *Caterpillars of British Butterflies.*
Stokoe, W. J. (compiler), *Caterpillars of British Moths.*
Clegg, J., *Freshwater Life of the British Isles.*
Ragge, D., *Grasshoppers, Crickets and Cockroaches of the British Isles.*
Southwood, T. R. E., *Life of Wayside and Woodland.*
Background reference.

Collins Natural History Series:
Bristowe, W. S., *World of Spiders.*
Macan, T. T., and Worthington, E. B., *Life in Lakes and Rivers.*
Ford, E. B., *Butterflies.*

Ford, E. B., *Moths.*
Butler, C. G., *World of the Honey Bee.*
Imms, A. D., *Insect Natural History.*
Background reference.

HMSO Bulletin No. 20, *Beneficial Insects*

School Natural Science Society Pamphlets:
Finch, I., *Common Spiders.*
Earthworms.
Identification Sheets:
Marson, E. J., *Insects and Other Land Arthropods;*
Marson, E. J., *Water Animals.*

Nuffield O-Level Biology: *Keys to small organisms in soil, litter and water troughs*, Longman and Penguin.
Nuffield Junior Science, *Animals and Plants*, Collins.

Books for the classroom

Allen, G., and Denslow, J., *Insects*, The Clue Books, Oxford University Press.
Clarke, M., *Snails, Caterpillars, Insects,* Observe and Learn Series, Rupert Hart Davies.
Doering, H., and McCormick, J., *An Ant is Born*, Sterling Nature Series, Oak Tree Press.
Gillespie, T. H., *Our Friends the Spiders,* Oliver and Boyd.

Goldin, A., *Spider Silk,* Black.
Hawes, J., *Watch Honey Bees with Me*, Black.
Haworth, F. M., *Garden Creatures, Wasps, Aquaria,* University of London Press.
Hirons, M. and D., *Insect Life of Farm and Garden,* Blandford Rural Studies Series Book 5. (*Able readers.*)
Laverie, S., *Wonders of the Ant Hill,* Wheaton.
Neal, C. D., *What is an Insect,* Collins.
Poole, L. and G., *Weird and Wonderful Ants,* Heinemann.
Ross, A., *Insects in Britain,* Blackwell.
Simon, S., *Discovering what Earthworms do*, World's Work Ltd.
Spoczynska, J., *A Zoo on your Windowledge,* Muller

How and Why: *Wonder Book of Ants and Bees.*

Junior True Books, *Spiders,* Muller.

Let's Read about Science Library: *Butterflies, Insects, Bees and Wasps,* Webster.

Macdonald Junior Reference Library: *Insects, Life in Fresh Water.*

Macdonald's First Library: *Insects that Live Together.*

Stand and Stare Books: *Grasshopper, Dragonfly, Daddy Longlegs, Ladybird, Butterfly, Earwig,* Methuen.

World of Nature Series, Book 3: *From Caterpillar to Butterfly (for the photographs).*

Objectives for children learning science

Guide lines to keep in mind

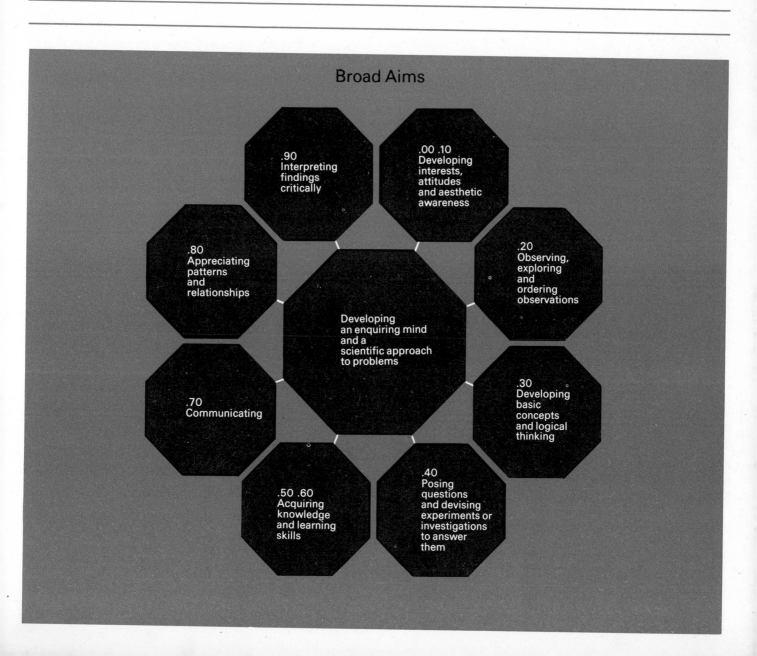

What we mean by Stage 1, Stage 2 and Stage 3

Attitudes, interests and aesthetic awareness

.00/.10

Stage 1
Transition from intuition to concrete operations. Infants generally.

The characteristics of thought among infant children differ in important respects from those of children over the age of about seven years. Infant thought has been described as 'intuitive' by Piaget; it is closely associated with physical action and is dominated by immediate observation. Generally, the infant is not able to think about or imagine the consequences of an action unless he has actually carried it out, nor is he yet likely to draw logical conclusions from his experiences. At this early stage the objectives are those concerned with active exploration of the immediate environment and the development of ability to discuss and communicate effectively: they relate to the kind of activities that are appropriate to these very young children, and which form an introduction to ways of exploring and of ordering observations.

1.01 Willingness to ask questions
1.02 Willingness to handle both living and non-living material.
1.03 Sensitivity to the need for giving proper care to living things.
1.04 Enjoyment in using all the senses for exploring and discriminating.
1.05 Willingness to collect material for observation or investigation.

Concrete operations. Early stage.

In this Stage, children are developing the ability to manipulate things mentally. At first this ability is limited to objects and materials that can be manipulated concretely, and even then only in a restricted way. The objectives here are concerned with developing these mental operations through exploration of concrete objects and materials—that is to say, objects and materials which, as physical things, have meaning for the child. Since older children, and even adults prefer an introduction to new ideas and problems through concrete example and physical exploration, these objectives are suitable for all children, whatever their age, who are being introduced to certain science activities for the first time.

1.06 Desire to find out things for oneself.
1.07 Willing participation in group work.
1.08 Willing compliance with safety regulations in handling tools and equipment.
1.09 Appreciation of the need to learn the meaning of new words and to use them correctly.

Stage 2
Concrete operations. Later stage.

In this Stage, a continuation of what Piaget calls the stage of concrete operations, the mental manipulations are becoming more varied and powerful. The developing ability to handle variables—for example, in dealing with multiple classification—means that problems can be solved in more ordered and quantitative ways than was previously possible. The objectives begin to be more specific to the exploration of the scientific aspects of the environment rather than to general experience, as previously. These objectives are developments of those of Stage 1 and depend on them for a foundation. They are those thought of as being appropriate for all children who have progressed from Stage 1 and not merely for nine- to eleven-year-olds.

2.01 Willingness to co-operate with others in science activities.
2.02 Willingness to observe objectively.
2.03 Appreciation of the reasons for safety regulations.
2.04 Enjoyment in examining ambiguity in the use of words.
2.05 Interest in choosing suitable means of expressing results and observations.
2.06 Willingness to assume responsibility for the proper care of living things.
2.07 Willingness to examine critically the results of their own and others' work.
2.08 Preference for putting ideas to test before accepting or rejecting them.
2.09 Appreciation that approximate methods of comparison may be more appropriate than careful measurements.

Stage 3
Transition to stage of abstract thinking.

This is the Stage in which, for some children, the ability to think about abstractions is developing. When this development is complete their thought is capable of dealing with the possible and hypothetical, and is not tied to the concrete and to the here and now. It may take place between eleven and thirteen for some able children, for some children it may happen later, and for others it may never occur. The objectives of this stage are ones which involve development of ability to use hypothetical reasoning and to separate and combine variables in a systematic way. They are appropriate to those who have achieved most of the Stage 2 objectives and who now show signs of ability to manipulate mentally ideas and propositions.

3.01 Acceptance of responsibility for their own and others' safety in experiments.
3.02 Preference for using words correctly.
3.03 Commitment to the idea of physical cause and effect.
3.04 Recognition of the need to standardise measurements.
3.05 Willingness to examine evidence critically.
3.06 Willingness to consider beforehand the usefulness of the results from a possible experiment.
3.07 Preference for choosing the most appropriate means of expressing results or observations.
3.08 Recognition of the need to acquire new skills.
3.09 Willingness to consider the role of science in everyday life.

Attitudes, interests and aesthetic awareness

.00/.10

Observing, exploring and ordering observations

.20

1.21 Appreciation of the variety of living things and materials in the environment.
1.22 Awareness of changes which take place as time passes.
1.23 Recognition of common shapes—square, circle, triangle.
1.24 Recognition of regularity in patterns.
1.25 Ability to group things consistently according to chosen or given criteria.

1.11 Awareness that there are various ways of testing out ideas and making observations.
1.12 Interest in comparing and classifying living or non-living things.
1.13 Enjoyment in comparing measurements with estimates.
1.14 Awareness that there are various ways of expressing results and observations.
1.15 Willingness to wait and to keep records in order to observe change in things.
1.16 Enjoyment in exploring the variety of living things in the environment.
1.17 Interest in discussing and comparing the aesthetic qualities of materials.

1.26 Awareness of the structure and form of living things.
1.27 Awareness of change of living things and non-living materials.
1.28 Recognition of the action of force
1.29 Ability to group living and non-living things by observable attributes.
1.29a Ability to distinguish regularity in events and motion.

2.11 Enjoyment in developing methods for solving problems or testing ideas.
2.12 Appreciation of the part that aesthetic qualities of materials play in determining their use.
2.13 Interest in the way discoveries were made in the past.

2.21 Awareness of internal structure in living and non-living things.
2.22 Ability to construct and use keys for identification.
2.23 Recognition of similar and congruent shapes.
2.24 Awareness of symmetry in shapes and structures.
2.25 Ability to classify living things and non-living materials in different ways.
2.26 Ability to visualise objects from different angles and the shape of cross-sections.

3.11 Appreciation of the main principles in the care of living things.
3.12 Willingness to extend methods used in science activities to other fields of experience.

3.21 Appreciation that classification criteria are arbitrary.
3.22 Ability to distinguish observations which are relevant to the solution of a problem from those which are not.
3.23 Ability to estimate the order of magnitude of physical quantities.

Developing basic concepts and logical thinking	Posing questions and devising experiments or investigations to answer them
.30	.40

Stage 1
Transition from intuition to concrete operations. Infants generally.

1.31 Awareness of the meaning of words which describe various types of quantity.
1.32 Appreciation that things which are different may have features in common.

1.41 Ability to find answers to simple problems by investigation.
1.42 Ability to make comparisons in terms of one property or variable.

- -

Concrete operations. Early stage.

1.33 Ability to predict the effect of certain changes through observation of similar changes.
1.34 Formation of the notions of the horizontal and the vertical.
1.35 Development of concepts of conservation of length and substance.
1.36 Awareness of the meaning of speed and of its relation to distance covered.

1.43 Appreciation of the need for measurement.
1.44 Awareness that more than one variable may be involved in a particular change.

Stage 2
Concrete operations. Later stage.

2.31 Appreciation of measurement as division into regular parts and repeated comparison with a unit.
2.32 Appreciation that comparisons can be made indirectly by use of an intermediary.
2.33 Development of concepts of conservation of weight, area and volume.
2.34 Appreciation of weight as a downward force.
2.35 Understanding of the speed, time, distance relation.

2.41 Ability to frame questions likely to be answered through investigations.
2.42 Ability to investigate variables and to discover effective ones.
2.43 Appreciation of the need to control variables and use controls in investigations.
2.44 Ability to choose and use either arbitrary or standard units of measurement as appropriate.
2.45 Ability to select a suitable degree of approximation and work to it.
2.46 Ability to use representational models for investigating problems or relationships.

Stage 3
Transition to stage of abstract thinking.

3.31 Familiarity with relationships involving velocity, distance, time, acceleration.
3.32 Ability to separate, exclude or combine variables in approaching problems.
3.33 Ability to formulate hypotheses not dependent upon direct observation.
3.34 Ability to extend reasoning beyond the actual to the possible.
3.35 Ability to distinguish a logically sound proof from others less sound.

3.41 Attempting to identify the essential steps in approaching a problem scientifically.
3.42 Ability to design experiments with effective controls for testing hypotheses.
3.43 Ability to visualise a hypothetical situation as a useful simplification of actual observations.
3.44 Ability to construct scale models for investigation and to appreciate implications of changing the scale.

1.51 Ability to discriminate between different materials.
1.52 Awareness of the characteristics of living things.
1.53 Awareness of properties which materials can have.
1.54 Ability to use displayed reference material for identifying living and non-living things.

1.55 Familiarity with sources of sound.
1.56 Awareness of sources of heat, light and electricity.
1.57 Knowledge that change can be produced in common substances.
1.58 Appreciation that ability to move or cause movement requires energy.
1.59 Knowledge of differences in properties between and within common groups of materials.

1.61 Appreciation of man's use of other living things and their products.
1.62 Awareness that man's way of life has changed through the ages.
1.63 Skill in manipulating tools and materials.
1.64 Development of techniques for handling living things correctly.
1.65 Ability to use books for supplementing ideas or information.

2.51 Knowledge of conditions which promote changes in living things and non-living materials.
2.52 Familiarity with a wide range of forces and of ways in which they can be changed.
2.53 Knowledge of sources and simple properties of common forms of energy.
2.54 Knowledge of the origins of common materials.
2.55 Awareness of some discoveries and inventions by famous scientists.
2.56 Knowledge of ways to investigate and measure properties of living things and non-living materials.
2.57 Awareness of changes in the design of measuring instruments and tools during man's history.
2.58 Skill in devising and constructing simple apparatus.
2.59 Ability to select relevant information from books or other reference material.

3.51 Knowledge that chemical change results from interaction.
3.52 Knowledge that energy can be stored and converted in various ways.
3.53 Awareness of the universal nature of gravity.
3.54 Knowledge of the main constituents and variations in the composition of soil and of the earth.
3.55 Knowledge that properties of matter can be explained by reference to its particulate nature.
3.56 Knowledge of certain properties of heat, light, sound, electrical, mechanical and chemical energy.
3.57 Knowledge of a wide range of living organisms.
3.58 Development of the concept of an internal environment.
3.59 Knowledge of the nature and variations in basic life processes.

3.61 Appreciation of levels of organisation in living things.
3.62 Appreciation of the significance of the work and ideas of some famous scientists.
3.63 Ability to apply relevant knowledge without help of contextual cues.
3.64 Ability to use scientific equipment and instruments for extending the range of human senses.

Communicating

.70

Appreciating patterns and relationships

.80

Stage 1

Transition from intuition to concrete operations. Infants generally.

1.71 Ability to use new words appropriately.
1.72 Ability to record events in their sequences.
1.73 Ability to discuss and record impressions of living and non-living things in the environment.
1.74 Ability to use representational symbols for recording information on charts or block graphs.

1.81 Awareness of cause-effect relationships.

Concrete operations. Early stage.

1.75 Ability to tabulate information and use tables.
1.76 Familiarity with names of living things and non-living materials.
1.77 Ability to record impressions by making models, painting or drawing.

1.82 Development of a concept of environment.
1.83 Formation of a broad idea of variation in living things.
1.84 Awareness of seasonal changes in living things.
1.85 Awareness of differences in physical conditions between different parts of the Earth.

Stage 2

Concrete operations. Later stage.

2.71 Ability to use non-representational symbols in plans, charts, etc.
2.72 Ability to interpret observations in terms of trends and rates of change.
2.73 Ability to use histograms and other simple graphical forms for communicating data.
2.74 Ability to construct models as a means of recording observations.

2.81 Awareness of sequences of change in natural phenomena.
2.82 Awareness of structure-function relationship in parts of living things.
2.83 Appreciation of interdependence among living things.
2.84 Awareness of the impact of man's activities on other living things.
2.85 Awareness of the changes in the physical environment brought about by man's activity.
2.86 Appreciation of the relationships of parts and wholes.

Stage 3

Transition to stage of abstract thinking.

3.71 Ability to select the graphical form most appropriate to the information being recorded.
3.72 Ability to use three-dimensional models or graphs for recording results.
3.73 Ability to deduce information from graphs: from gradient, area, intercept.
3.74 Ability to use analogies to explain scientific ideas and theories.

3.81 Recognition that the ratio of volume to surface area is significant.
3.82 Appreciation of the scale of the universe.
3.83 Understanding of the nature and significance of changes in living and non-living things.
3.84 Recognition that energy has many forms and is conserved when it is changed from one form to another.
3.85 Recognition of man's impact on living things—conservation, change, control.
3.86 Appreciation of the social implications of man's changing use of materials, historical and contemporary.
3.87 Appreciation of the social implications of research in science.
3.88 Appreciation of the role of science in the changing pattern of provision for human needs.

Interpreting findings critically

.90

1.91   Awareness that the apparent size, shape and relationships of things depend on the position of the observer.

- -

1.92   Appreciation that properties of materials influence their use.

2.91   Appreciation of adaptation to environment.
2.92   Appreciation of how the form and structure of materials relate to their function and properties.
2.93   Awareness that many factors need to be considered when choosing a material for a particular use.
2.94   Recognition of the role of chance in making measurements and experiments.

These Stages we have chosen conform to modern ideas about children's learning. They conveniently describe for us the mental development of children between the ages of five and thirteen years, but it must be remembered that ALTHOUGH CHILDREN GO THROUGH THESE STAGES IN THE SAME ORDER THEY DO NOT GO THROUGH THEM AT THE SAME RATES.
SOME children achieve the later Stages at an early age.
SOME loiter in the early Stages for quite a time.
SOME never have the mental ability to develop to the later Stages.
ALL appear to be ragged in their movement from one Stage to another.
Our Stages, then, are not tied to chronological age, so in any one class of children there will be, almost certainly, some children at differing Stages of mental development.

3.91   Ability to draw from observations conclusions that are unbiased by preconception.
3.92   Willingness to accept factual evidence despite perceptual contradictions.
3.93   Awareness that the degree of accuracy of measurements has to be taken into account when results are interpreted.
3.94   Awareness that unstated assumptions can affect conclusions drawn from argument or experimental results.
3.95   Appreciation of the need to integrate findings into a simplifying generalisation.
3.96   Willingness to check that conclusions are consistent with further evidence.

Index

Illustration acknowledgements:

The publishers gratefully acknowledge the help given by the following in supplying photographs on the pages indicated:

Bruce Coleman, Photographer: S. C. Bisserot, 16, 32 left, 50 left, 58; Photographer: Russ Kinne, 9; Photographer: S. C. Porter, 14
Imperial Chemical Industries Limited, 49
James Wright, 4, 5, 22, 24, 30 left, 33, 36 top and bottom right, 37, 40, 44, 45, 50, 51, 53, 54, 55, 61, 62, 74, 75
Medway College of Design, Photographer: Sarah Blythe, 27, 29
Natural History Photographic Agency, 35, 42; Photographer: Andrew E. Carr, 15
Peter J. Green, 32 top, 38
Plant Protection Limited, 48 bottom
Shell Photographic Service, 32 right, 48 top, 56; Photographer: Clive Cadwallader, 47
South West Picture Agency, 11, 19, 20, 30 right, 31, 33 left, 36 bottom left, 38, 58 left, 62 right, 71

Line drawings: The Garden Studio, Anna Barnard

Identification charts: Cynthia O'Brien

Labelling and flow charts: GWA Design Consultants Ltd

Cover design: Peter Gauld